children in mind

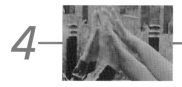

1 — The Changing Context

Commissioners and providers of child and adolescent mental health services (CAMHS) face a growing agenda for change.

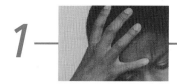

2 — The Children

Children requiring specialist CAMHS present with a wide range of complex problems.

3 — A Variable Response

Children face wide variation when it comes to getting a service in terms of both levels of spending, the services and staff available, links with other agencies and access to services.

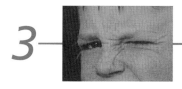

4 — Working Together

Health and local authorities, together with service providers, must assess children's needs for CAMHS, take stock of current provision, and translate outstanding needs into service requirements.

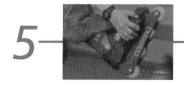

5 — Moving Forward

Action is needed at both national and local levels so that all agencies can emulate the best in terms of providing the most effective and co-ordinated services.

Contents

© Audit Commission 1999

First published in September 1999 by the Audit Commission for Local Authorities
and the National Health Service in England and Wales, 1 Vincent Square,
London SW1P 2PN

Printed in the UK for the Audit Commission by Holbrooks Printers, Portsmouth

ISBN 186240 160 8

Photographs: Paul Doyle/Photofusion (p50), Don Gray/Photofusion (p72),
Pam Isherwood/Format (p14), David Mansell (pp52, 77), Jenny Matthews/Format
(p64), Maggie Murray/Format (pp4, 59), Fiona Pragoff/Collections (p3),
Ulrike Preuss/Format (cover – posed by model), Brenda Prince/Format (p17),
Hilary Shedel (p31), Anthea Sieveking (p46), Paula Solloway/Format (p19)

The Audit Commission does not intend to imply that the young people depicted in the
photographs used throughout this report are suffering from mental health problems.

Preface

The Audit Commission oversees the external audit of local authorities and the National Health Service in England and Wales. As part of this function, the Commission is required to undertake audits to enable it to make recommendations for improving the economy, efficiency and effectiveness of services provided by these bodies. Over the last two years, the Commission has been conducting a national audit of the specialist child and adolescent mental health services (CAMHS) provided by health authorities and trusts. These agencies have all received a local report summarising the issues that are pertinent to them, following an approach devised by the Commission which uses data collection instruments that have been processed centrally to generate local comparative information. This report summarises the information from these audits and the issues and conclusions reached by local auditors.

The Commission's team consisted of Claire Blackman, Mel Shaw, Philip Blake, Louise Cloke, Rodney Vardey and Tom Dixon under the direction of David Browning. Particular thanks go to our external adviser, Dr Zarrina Kurtz, who has made a major contribution throughout and provided much of the key material for this report. She has provided effective direction and encouragement in equal measure. Thanks also go to our external advisers' group (listed at Appendix 1), which has given direction, support and help both at periodic group meetings and through private correspondence; to Kit Harbottle who played a major part in shaping the audit; and finally to Professor Richard Williams who has provided comment and guidance on the report.

However, the main thanks go to the staff of CAMHS throughout England and Wales who took the time and trouble to complete the data collection instruments, and who sometimes waited a long time for comparative data because of difficulties in processing the data centrally. The staff who helped to pilot the approach deserve particular thanks for their patience. If the report helps to advance the cause of CAMHS and the children and young people who depend on them, it is mainly due to their efforts. Any errors, however, are the responsibility of the Commission alone.

1

The Changing Context

Mental health problems lead to considerable distress in children and young people and their families, and can have far-reaching effects. The NHS, local authorities and the voluntary and independent sectors all provide services. A large agenda of policy and practice development is providing a major challenge for all these agencies.

The scale and types of problem

1. Over the past 20 years, the importance of the mental health of children and adolescents has been increasingly recognised, and a wide variety of disorders described [TABLE 1] (Ref.1). Recent studies agree fairly closely that about one in five children and adolescents suffer from a wide range of mental health problems[1] (Ref. 2), and that this proportion has increased – certainly in industrialised countries – since the end of the Second World War (Ref. 3) (Appendix 2).

2. Compared with the high profile given to mental illness in adults, the significance of the mental health of children and adolescents has been recognised only recently. Previously, problems were often dismissed as 'growing pains' and left for parents to deal with. This view has changed, partly because of a growth in knowledge about the emotional and psychological development of children (Ref. 4), and partly because of a growing awareness of the wide implications of emotional and behavioural disturbance in young people (Ref. 2). Strong links have been established between mental health problems in children and young people and many issues of growing public concern, such as juvenile crime, alcohol and drug misuse, self-harm, and eating disorders (Ref. 3).

---

1   The term 'mental health problem' has been used generically in this report to cover a range of types and severity of psychological and psychiatric difficulties and disorders that are experienced by children and young people.

TABLE 1

A classification of mental disorders	Examples
Emotional disorders	Phobias, anxiety states and depression. These may be made manifest in physical symptoms such as chronic headache or abdominal pain.
Conduct disorders	Stealing, defiance, fire-setting, aggression and antisocial behaviour.
Hyper-kinetic disorders	Disturbance of activity and attention.
Development disorders	Delay in acquiring certain skills such as speech, bladder control and social ability. These disorders may affect one area of development, or pervade a number of areas, as in children with autism.
Eating disorders	Pre-school eating problems, anorexia nervosa and bulimia nervosa.
Habit disorders	Tics, sleeping problems and soiling.
Post-traumatic syndromes	Post-traumatic stress disorder.
Somatic disorders	Chronic fatigue syndrome.
Psychotic disorders	Schizophrenia, manic depressive disorder or drug-induced psychoses.

Source: Ref. 1

The rate of mental health problems is high in young offenders, particularly persistent offenders

3. Although children from all backgrounds may suffer from mental health problems, the proportion is higher where children and their families live in disadvantaged circumstances – in some inner-city areas for example (Ref. 5). The level of increased risk has been estimated in many instances (Ref. 6), and the likelihood of mental health disorder has been found to increase with increasing numbers of risk factors (Ref. 7). Some children are particularly vulnerable. For example, two-thirds of young people looked after by the local authority in Oxfordshire were found to have a diagnosable psychiatric disorder, compared with 15 per cent living with their own families (Ref. 8). Those with a parent with a mental illness are also known to be at high risk of developing a mental health difficulty of their own (Ref. 9).

4. The rate of mental health problems is high in young offenders, particularly persistent offenders (Ref. 10). A diagnosis of a primary mental disorder was found in one-third of young men aged between 16 and 18 years sentenced by a court (Ref. 11); and screening of 10 to 17 year olds attending a city centre youth court revealed disturbingly high levels of both psychiatric and physical morbidity, including learning difficulties, mood disorders, epilepsy, frequent use of alcohol and illicit drugs, and mental illness (Ref. 12).

5. Children who do not do well at school, whether because of low IQ or a specific learning disorder, are at increased risk of mental health problems, which may be as high as 40 per cent (Ref. 13). Difficult behaviour is the most common reason for children to be excluded from school, and the risks of further mental health problems are high among these children (Ref. 14). In a national survey, behavioural problems were found to be the most common disabling condition that limited the capacity of children aged up to 15 to carry out daily activities (Ref. 15). Poor school results, and the low self-esteem that they create, can affect future employment prospects and increase the risk of further psychological problems. Friendships may be difficult, leading to social isolation which can make things worse. The chances of making satisfying long-term relationships may suffer and the ability to act as a competent parent may be undermined, increasing the risk that a cycle of psychological and social problems will be repeated in the next generation.

6. Mental health problems lead to considerable distress in children and families. While some of these problems are relatively mild and self-limiting, others can be life-threatening. A significant number of severe problems in childhood, if not adequately treated, lead to lifelong mental illness in adulthood (Ref. 2). Emotional and behavioural difficulties in the young not only carry an increased probability of adult mental illness, they also may indicate an increased risk of delinquency as the child grows up, and continuing antisocial behaviour in adulthood (Ref. 16).

Providers of services

7. Services for the mental health of children and adolescents are provided not only by the NHS but also by local authority social services, education, youth justice and other departments, voluntary organisations, and the independent sector. They range from general primary care services to highly specialist services, which may not be located in every district in the country.

8. These services have been described within the framework of a four-tier model. In this model, each tier essentially addresses different types of problem with the level of severity increasing from Tier 1 to Tier 4 [EXHIBIT 1]. This conceptual model has been promoted by the Department of Health (Ref. 17), and is evolving to reflect changes in thinking and practice (Ref. 18).

EXHIBIT 1

Key components, professionals and functions of tiered CAMHS

Mental health services for children and adolescents have been described according to a four-tier framework.

Tier 1
A primary level, which includes interventions by:

- GPs
- Health visitors
- Residential social workers
- Juvenile justice workers
- School nurses
- Teachers

These non-specialist staff:

- identify mental health problems early in their development
- offer general advice – and, in certain cases, treatment for less severe mental health problems
- pursue opportunities for promoting mental health and preventing mental health problems

Tier 2
A level of service provided by professionals working on their own who relate to others through a network rather than within a team:

- Clinical child psychologists
- Educational psychologists
- Paediatricians – especially community
- Community child psychiatric nurses or nurse specialists
- Child psychiatrists

CAMHS professionals offer:

- training and consultation to other professionals (who might be within Tier 1)
- consultation for professionals and families
- outreach to identify severe or complex needs where children or families are unwilling to use specialist services
- assessment which may trigger treatment at this level or in a different tier

Tier 3
A specialist service for the more severe, complex and persistent disorders:

- Social workers
- Clinical psychologists
- Community psychiatric nurses
- Child and adolescent psychiatrists
- Art, music and drama therapists
- Child psychotherapists
- Occupational therapists

This is usually a multidisciplinary team or service working in a community child mental health clinic or child psychiatry outpatient service and offering:

- assessment and treatment of child mental health disorders
- assessment for referrals to Tier 4
- contributions to the services, consultation and training at Tiers 1 and 2
- participation in research and development projects

Tier 4
Infrequently used but essential tertiary services such as day units, highly specialised outpatient teams, and inpatient units for older children and adolescents who are severely mentally ill or at suicidal risk.

Source: Ref. 17 – Table 4

9. Many services are provided at Tier 1 – by general practitioners (GPs), health visitors and other primary healthcare staff, teachers, social workers and voluntary agencies. In this tier, services are delivered as part of a wider function – for instance, a teacher counselling a persistent truant. The other three tiers make up the specialist child and adolescent mental health services (CAMHS). At Tier 2, professionals tend to work on their own. At Tier 3, specialists from various disciplines and agencies work together – co-ordinated in teams or otherwise. Tier 4 comprises highly specialised services, such as inpatient facilities. This report focuses on the specialist services at Tiers 2, 3 and 4, that are provided by the National Health Service (NHS). A number of studies have shown that between 10 and 20 per cent of children with mental health problems are seen by specialist mental health professionals (Refs. 19 and 20).

10. Information from the audits of both health authority commissioners and specialist CAMHS providers indicates that about £150 million is spent on specialist CAMHS in England and Wales each year. Specialist CAMHS are provided in about 160 NHS trusts across England and Wales. These services are usually a small part of each of these trusts' overall activity.

Recent developments in policy and practice

11. The policy agenda for addressing the mental health problems of children and young people has been developing rapidly in the NHS, and growing at a similar pace in local authorities [BOX A]. Over the past five years, more has been learnt from research and service evaluation in CAMHS and the knowledge base is growing all the time. The evidence covers the causes and complexity of factors associated with mental health problems and their impact.

BOX A

Recent developments in policy and practice

1993/1994

A National Review of services in England (Ref. 21) found wide variation in the type and level of resources among all relevant agencies.

1994

The Department for Education issued *Pupils with Problems*, a set of six circulars and guidance on good practice which described problems from naughtiness through emotional and behavioural difficulties to mental illness (Ref. 22).

1995

A handbook on CAMHS was published by the Departments of Health and Education, supporting the concept of a multidisciplinary, multi-agency approach (Ref. 17).

The NHS Health Advisory Service published *Together We Stand* (Ref. 1), a major guide to commissioning and delivering CAMHS.

The Department of Health issued *Child Protection: Messages from Research* which showed the importance of paying attention to children's emotional needs (Ref. 23).

1996

New guidance was issued for including CAMHS within Children's Services Plans (Ref. 24).

1996/1997

The NHS Executive included child and adolescent mental health in its *Priorities and Planning Guidance* as one of six areas to be monitored over three years (Ref. 25).

BOX A (continued)

1997

The Parliamentary Health Select Committee issued a report on CAMHS, and stressed the particular importance of Tier 1 services and the need for agencies to work together. It also commented on the paucity of routine information about CAMHS (Ref. 26).

The Welsh Office published *The Health of Children in Wales* (Ref. 27).

A new government interdepartmental social exclusion unit was established. This highlighted the importance of early involvement with children at risk of exclusion from school and of youth crime.

1998

Research by the Welsh Office found the same wide variations in services in Wales reported for England in the Review of 1993/94 (Ref. 28).

A major initiative *Meeting Special Educational Needs: a Programme for Action* stressed the need to prevent exclusion from school, and required local authorities to set up multi-agency behaviour support plans (Ref. 29).

The Crime and Disorder Act established the Youth Justice Board and introduced youth offending teams to start in April 2000.

The Parliamentary Health Select Committee issued a report on children 'looked after' by local authorities and reported on the failure of specialist mental health services to support them (Ref 30).

In England, the Quality Protects programme was launched to ensure that local authority social services for children are well-managed and effective (Ref. 31).

A consultation paper, *Supporting Families*, was published in November 1998 setting out proposals for providing better support to parents and families. The paper included proposals for a new family and parenting institute, a new national parent helpline and an expanded role for health visitors.

The Sure Start programme was introduced to extend and integrate services for children under 4 in areas of disadvantage. The aim is to ensure they are healthy, confident and thriving when they arrive at school.

The English Green Paper on Public Health (Ref. 33) focused on reducing health inequalities (Ref. 34). Mental health was one of four priority areas, and the paper commented that 'early action in a child's life may improve their health and mental health in later life'.

The equivalent Welsh Green Paper stated that 'the Welsh Office intends to focus on children's health and wellbeing as an investment in the future, and will build on The Health of Children in Wales 1997 to develop a comprehensive strategy to improve children's health'.

1998/1999

In England, the Mental Illness Specific Grant (now known as the Mental Health Grant) includes a designated component for child mental health for the first time (Ref. 35).

1999

The Department of Health announced an extra £84 million for development of CAMHS, spread over three years, and issued a circular setting out how these funds were to be used (Ref. 35).

In Wales, a multidisciplinary advisory group has been set up to draw up an all-Wales strategy for CAMHS. In addition senior nurses in Wales are looking at nursing standards in CAMHS.

1999/2000

National Priorities Guidance (Ref. 36) was directed at local authorities and health services jointly for the first time. Social services are to lead on children's welfare and interagency working; and they are to share the lead with health authorities on mental health and cutting health inequalities.

2000

During 2000, the results of a national morbidity survey carried out by the Office of National Statistics will become available, and will describe mental health problems and disorders in children in England and Wales linked to information about service use.

A systematic review of the literature funded by the NHS Research and Development Programme will be published (Ref. 37).

Good practice guidance

12. Complementing this fast-moving agenda, a number of ways of working that constitute good practice have been described in recent years. In 1992, *With Health in Mind* (Ref. 38) – primarily a voluntary sector initiative – developed a set of criteria for a good service with a strong user and carer focus. These criteria were developed further following a national survey (Ref. 21). Detailed guidelines were set out in the NHS Health Advisory Service report *Together We Stand* (Ref. 1). Principles for models of care were further identified in a guide to needs assessment (Ref. 6). Criteria for good practice in commissioning and provision were summarised in the handbook published jointly by the DoH and the DfE in 1995 (Ref. 17). Critical review of what constitutes good practice is underway. As an example, the Health Advisory Service 2000 is developing and piloting standards with the Research Unit of the Royal College of Psychiatrists.

13. Drawing upon these sources, good practice should be based on:

- evidence from the scientific literature about what works;
- equitable access;
- service acceptability to enable optimal compliance with treatment and management;
- maintenance of staff skills and morale;
- planned and agreed prioritisation of cases;
- management of the whole child and of relevant contextual factors;
- maximum participation of the child or young person in decisions with full consideration given to their wishes; and
- optimal use of expensive resources.

14. The Commission has incorporated the main features of this body of work into a checklist so that commissioners, providers and others can evaluate their own practices (Appendix 3).

Reviewing progress

15. Over two years between 1997 and 1999, the Audit Commission has been assessing progress with the implementation of this agenda. This report sets out the findings. An early concern of the Audit Commission was a serious lack of data about CAMHS at Tiers 2, 3 and 4. At the start of the study, it was difficult to find such basic facts as the number of trusts providing services, the amount of money spent on them and the number and type of staff employed. To help make good this deficit, the audit was structured to collect data from health authorities and trusts to form the basis of benchmarks for their local use.

16. The Audit Commission has carried out audit work in 59 health authorities and 147 NHS trusts. This means that it had reviewed, by 1st June 1999, approximately 60 per cent of the health authorities commissioning CAMHS in England and Wales, and over 90 per cent of the NHS trusts providing CAMHS at Tiers 2,3, and 4. Appendix 4 summarises the audit objectives, and describes the audit methodology. The main part of the audit was carried out by means of questionnaires that were designed specifically for the health authorities and for the trusts. In most of the trusts that completed the trust questionnaire (and in 23 others), extra information was also collected directly from professionals who provided details of their work by completing a diary over a four-week period; some also collected and reported details of each child they saw. In 92 trusts, professionals also documented the problems of the children presenting to them. The databases are listed [TABLE 2], and maps detailing the coverage of the audits are included on the next two pages [MAPS 1 and 2, overleaf].

17. Chapter 2 describes the children and young people who presented to specialist CAMHS throughout England and Wales during a four-week sample period. Chapter 3 describes the way CAMHS currently respond. Chapter 4 indicates the tasks that must be undertaken to take services forward. Chapter 5 summarises the challenges for the future if services are to keep pace with developments in policy and practice.

TABLE 2

The Audit Commission databases

	Number of questionnaires	Number of trusts	Number of children[I]	Number of staff
1. Health authority questionnaire database	59	–	–	–
2. Trust questionnaire database	124	124	–	–
3. Trust scanned data: diaries database	–	119	–	2,902
4. Trust scanned data: case characteristics database	–	114	31,032	–
5. Trust scanned data: presenting problems database	–	92	25,282	–

I   The numbers shown are the numbers of separate children presenting to CAMHS during the four-week period. The terms 'present to' and 'present with' are used throughout the report to convey the idea of a child who is referred to CAMHS for an assessment, evaluation or examination.

MAP 1

Audits carried out in NHS trusts

Most of the trusts that completed the questionnaire also collected extra information direct from professionals.

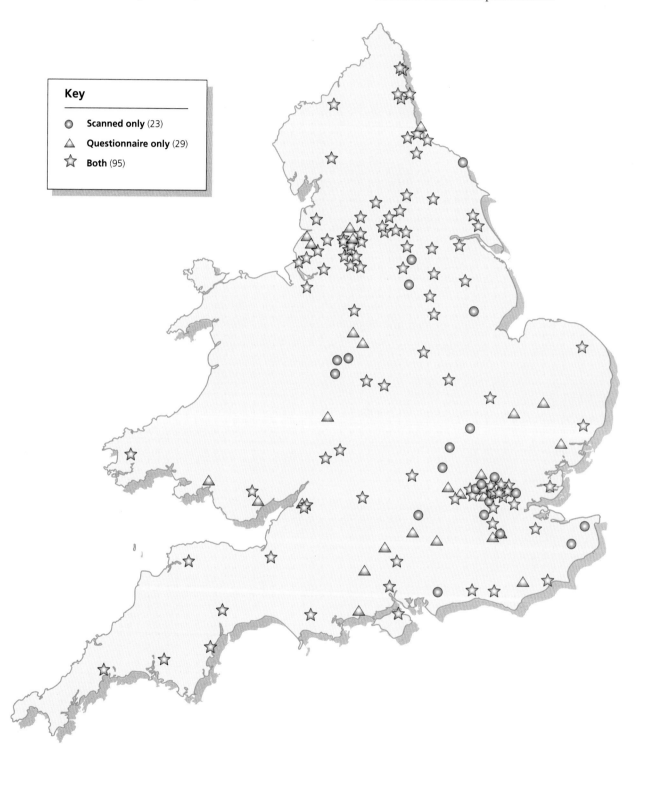

Key

⊙	**Scanned only** (23)
△	**Questionnaire only** (29)
☆	**Both** (95)

Source: Audit Commission

MAP 2

Audits carried out in health authorities

Approximately 60 per cent of the health authorities in England and Wales contributed to the audit.

Key

Completed health
authority questionnaire

Source: Audit Commission

2—

The Children

The young people who need the help of specialist child and adolescent mental health services present with a wide range of problems, many of which are complex and severe. Boys outnumber girls overall, although from mid-teens girls outnumber boys. Certain groups of children, and those living in certain conditions, present with mental health problems in disproportionate numbers.

18. This chapter describes the children who presented over the four-week period of the audits (Appendix 4). These children came from a wide variety of localities (inner-city, urban, and rural) across England and Wales.

Characteristics of children and young people using CAMHS

19. Boys outnumbered girls overall[1] and particularly in the younger age groups [EXHIBIT 2]. After mid-teens more girls were seen by CAMHS than boys. Just 3 per cent of the children and young people seen in CAMHS were cared for as inpatients; most of these were teenagers, and by far the highest number were girls between the ages of 15 and 18 [EXHIBIT 3, overleaf]. More girls were seen in inpatient settings than boys.

20. Professionals recorded their opinion about the ethnic origin of the children presenting. Overall, the sample case-mix comprised 12.5 per cent non-white children. The 1991 Census showed that the non-white population of children under 14 was 9.7 per cent (Ref. 39). This suggests that, overall, CAMHS is seeing at least a representative number of children from minority backgrounds. Where local minority populations are high, the CAMHS caseloads reflect this: two trusts in Manchester and in London, where the non-white local child population was known to be high were examined. The non-white component of the CAMHS caseload was 35 per cent in the Manchester trust compared with its non-white child catchment population of 13 per cent, while in the London trust, just over 50 per cent of the cases were non-white, compared with the local non-white child population of 36 per cent.

---

[1]   Actual proportions were 39 per cent girls (11,977), and 61 per cent boys (18,877) – total children with completed age and gender details 30,854.

EXHIBIT 2

Age bands of all children and young people seen by specialist CAMHS

Boys outnumbered girls overall.

Number of children

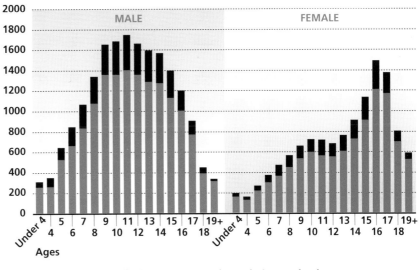

Source: Audit Commission case characteristics database

EXHIBIT 3

Age bands of children and young people seen by CAMHS in inpatient settings

Just 3 per cent of the children and young people, mainly teenagers, were seen as inpatients.

Number of children

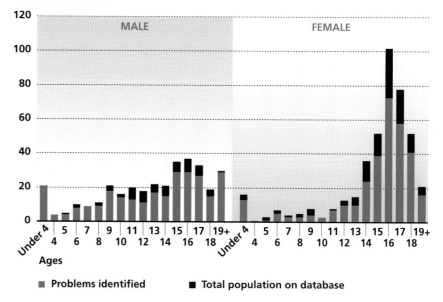

Ages

■ Problems identified   ■ Total population on database

Source: Audit Commission case characteristics database

Problems presented

21. The children and young people presented with a range of problems. To describe these, the Audit Commission adopted the Health of the Nation Outcome Scales for Children and Adolescents (HoNOSCA (Ref. 40) (Appendix 5). These scales cover 13 categories of problem,[I] each with four degrees of severity from 1 (the least severe) to 4 (the most severe). For the purposes of the analyses described in this report, ratings 1 and 2 are referred to as 'moderate problems',[II] and 3 and 4 as 'severe problems'.

I The original HoNOSCA scale has 15 categories, but the Audit Commission variant used only the first 13. HoNOSCA was designed primarily to measure change in presenting problems and functioning. The Audit Commission used HoNOSCA to obtain a snapshot of problems presenting to CAMHS professionals, rather than to record changes in these problems over time.

II On the assumption that a problem must be considered at least 'moderate' to have reached a CAMHS specialist.

22. Details of the problems presenting were recorded over the four-week study period [**EXHIBIT 4**]. For any young person, more than one category of problem could be recorded. The four categories that presented most frequently (in 60 to 80 per cent of children and young people) were:

- problems with family life and relationships;
- problems involving emotional and related symptoms (including eating disorders);
- problems with peer relationships; and
- disruptive, antisocial or aggressive behaviour.

EXHIBIT 4

Types and severity of problems recorded

Four types of problem were each present in between 60 and 80 per cent of children.

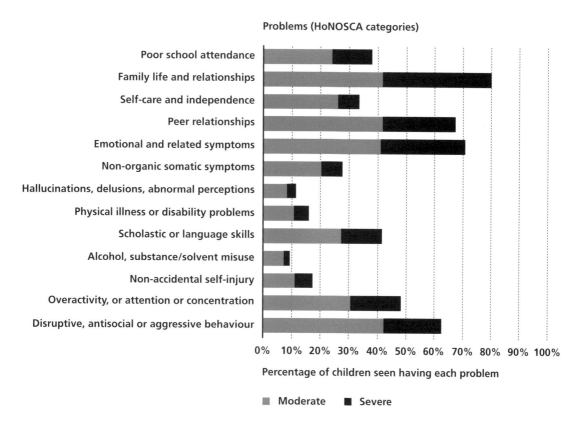

Problems (HoNOSCA categories)

Percentage of children seen having each problem

■ Moderate ■ Severe

Source: Audit Commission presenting problems database

23. Fewer than 5 per cent of children presented with only one problem category within HoNOSCA; the remainder had more than one. The most frequent number of problems found was five, but some children had more [EXHIBIT 5]. Exactly half the children had no or just one problem ranked as severe, 18 per cent had two problems in the severe category and 32 per cent had three or more [EXHIBIT 6].

EXHIBIT 5

Children presenting with more than one category of problem

The most frequent number of problems was five, but some children had more.

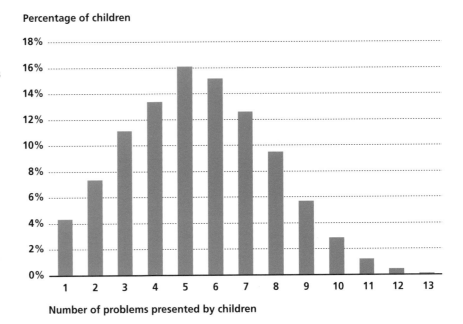

Percentage of children

Number of problems presented by children

Source: Audit Commission presenting problems database

EXHIBIT 6

The severity of presenting problems

Exactly half the children had no or just one problem rated as severe, and almost one-third had three or more problems in the severe category.

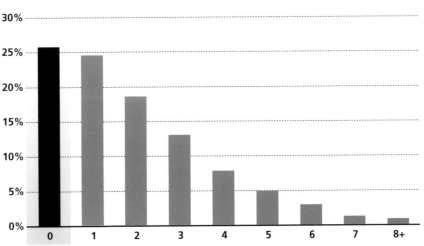

Percentage of children

Number of problems rated as severe

Source: Audit Commission presenting problems database

24. Different problems occurred with different frequencies. But, although CAMHS saw more boys than girls, the categories of problems presented by girls once they reached CAMHS were similar to those presented by boys. For instance, more boys than girls were seen by CAMHS who were considered to be disruptive, aggressive and antisocial (HoNOSCA category 1); but once a girl had reached CAMHS, there was broadly the same likelihood that she would be considered to be disruptive, aggressive or antisocial [**EXHIBIT 7**].

25. There was some variation between trusts in terms of their case-mix. The level of children considered by their supervising professional to exhibit characteristics that fit HoNOSCA category 1 averaged 62 per cent across all participating trusts. But the figure was below 50 per cent in five trusts, and exceeded 70 per cent in four [**EXHIBIT 8, overleaf**].

EXHIBIT 7

The proportion of children and young people with disruptive, aggressive and antisocial behaviour (HoNOSCA category 1)

Although CAMHS see more boys than girls, the problems presented by girls, once they reach CAMHS, are similar to those presented by boys.

Number of children seen

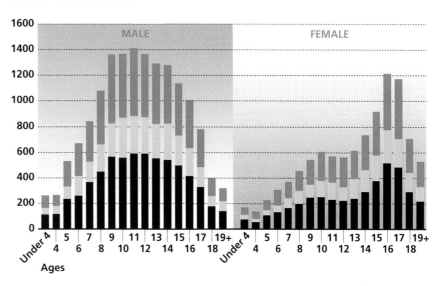

■ All CAMHS who did casework and problems – all conditions 1-13
HoNOSCA 1-Moderate   ■ HoNOSCA 1-Severe

Source: Audit Commission presenting problems database

EXHIBIT 8

The proportion of children and young people with disruptive, aggressive and antisocial behaviour (HoNOSCA category 1) in different trusts

The proportion of children with these behaviour problems ranged across trusts from below 50 per cent to above 70 per cent.

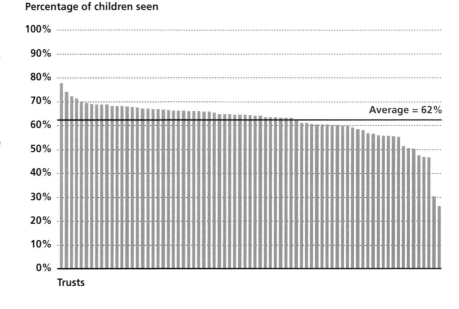

Percentage of children seen

Average = 62%

Trusts

Source: Audit Commission presenting problems database

Children at greater risk of developing mental health problems

26. Certain groups of children, and those living in certain conditions, are at greater risk of developing mental health problems than others (paragraphs 3 to 5 and Appendix 2). Factors known to be associated with children's vulnerability to the development of mental health problems were recorded in the audits using a scale based in part on the 'Paddington Complexity Score' (Ref. 41).

27. Certain factors occurred more frequently than others among the children presenting to specialist CAMHS [EXHIBIT 9]. The audits discovered that:

- 40 per cent were living with only one natural parent – either with a lone parent or with a step-parent in a re-constituted family – compared with around 21 per cent of all families with dependent children in Great Britian in 1996 (Ref. 42);

- 34 per cent were living in families where the main breadwinner was unemployed – well above the national average;

- 27 per cent had some form of learning disability;

- 19 per cent were living with a parent with mental illness;[1] and

- 9 per cent of children were looked after by the local authority – compared with 0.5 per cent in the general population (Ref. 44).

---

[1] It is known that about 10 per cent of adults in the total population have a mental health problem that has been identified by a GP, and that about 3 per cent receive treatment from specialist adult mental health services (Ref. 43). It is not known how many of these adults are parents of young people. It is also unknown how many children live in a family which includes an adult with a mental health problem, although it is extremely unlikely that it is as high as the 19 per cent found in the Audit Commission 'case characteristics database'.

EXHIBIT 9

Complexity factors

Certain groups of children are at greater risk of developing mental health problems.

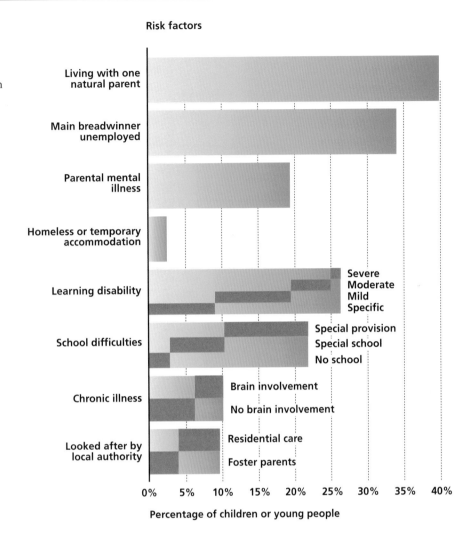

Risk factors

Source: Audit Commission case characteristics database

28. As has been reported in previous research studies (Refs. 45 and 46), children frequently present to specialist services with more than one problem and several complexity factors. In the audit sample, only about 20 per cent of children had no complexity factors [EXHIBIT 10, overleaf]. Also, the number of factors was no different for different age groups.

EXHIBIT 10

Multiple complexity factors

Children and young people often present with more than one factor – and the number of factors is fairly consistent across all ages.

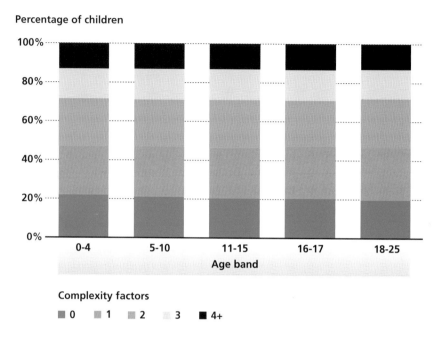

Percentage of children

Complexity factors

■ 0   ■ 1   ■ 2   ▫ 3   ■ 4+

Source: Audit Commission case characteristics database

Conclusion

29. Authorities and trusts must take account of the range of problems with which children present to the specialist services, and the level and distribution of children at particular risk, in order to understand local needs and to evaluate how well their services are adjusted to meet these needs. The current pattern of service response is described in the next chapter.

3

A Variable Response

Health authorities should review the resources that they provide for CAMHS, matching needs with a specifically designated budget. Trusts should review their staffing arrangements to make sure that they have sufficient skills to respond effectively. They should improve the way that they work with, and support, other agencies. To ensure that they provide good access for children and young people, trusts need to review referral routes and arrangements, waiting times, and systems for emergency cover.

30. Health authorities and trusts need to be able to respond effectively and efficiently to the needs of the children and young people described in the previous chapter. The national survey of services for the mental health of children and young people carried out in England in 1993/94 found wide variations in their ability to do so (Ref. 21). The Commission's audits found that variation between services is still significant, causing difficulties for staff and children alike.

Variations in resources

31. The amount spent by health authorities on specialist CAMHS per head of child population aged up to 18 was found to vary by a factor of seven [EXHIBIT 11]. The variation showed little relation to local needs, as measured by the 'Jarman index' of socio-economic deprivation (Ref. 47) [EXHIBIT 12].

32. Most of this variation is more readily explained by historical spending patterns than as a response to needs, as some authorities and trusts did not have a grip on their patterns of expenditure on specialist CAMHS. One-third of trusts did not have a complete understanding of the sources of income for their specialist CAMHS. The amount that health authorities said that they spent on trusts did not always tally with the amount that trusts said that they received from health authorities.

EXHIBIT 11

Health authority expenditure per head of the child population aged up to 18

The amount spent by health authorities on specialist CAMHS varied by a factor of seven.

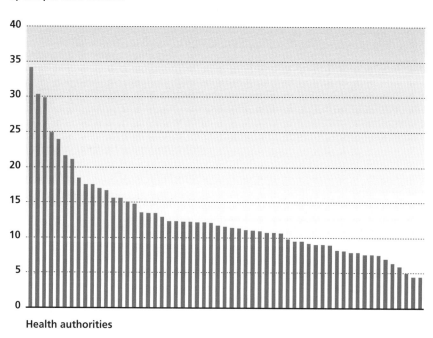

Spend per child head £s

Health authorities

Source: Audit Commission health authority questionnaires

24

33. These discrepancies probably occur for a number of reasons. First, CAMHS usually represents only a small percentage of expenditure on mental health.[I] Second, inaccuracies may occur where no systematic attempt has been made beforehand to apportion costs between CAMHS and adult services.[II] And third, the absence of a designated manager may mean that there is no one to identify clearly what is spent on CAMHS. If CAMHS are to be improved, an important first step must be to take stock of how much is being spent on these services now, and to set up a separate budget where none currently exists.

I   The audits showed that health authority funding of CAMHS accounted, on average, for around 5 per cent of total mental health spend across England and Wales. Adult services absorbed approximately 95 per cent of the NHS mental health budgets.

II   Some part of CAMHS may be administered and budgeted as part of the adult service – for example, child and adolescent psychiatrists may be covered by an overall staffing budget for the trust, rather than in a disaggregated CAMHS budget. And clinical psychology is often provided and managed quite separately from the rest of CAMHS.

EXHIBIT 12

Health authority expenditure in relation to an indicator of needs

There is little relationship between expenditure and needs.

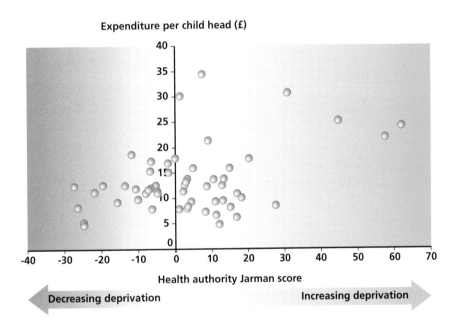

Expenditure per child head (£)

Health authority Jarman score

Decreasing deprivation   Increasing deprivation

Sources: Audit Commission health authority questionnaires and the Underprivileged Area Score (Ref. 47)

Health authorities should be monitoring demand as part of their assessment of the level of resources needed, and should evaluate the cause and extent of any fluctuations in demand

34. Many trusts told auditors of pressure from rising numbers of referrals with no adjustment in resources to meet this demand. However, almost one-third of the trusts audited could not produce figures to back this claim. Information from 85 trusts which did maintain summary data to describe trends in workload suggests that while there had been significant increases in referrals accepted on to caseloads for CAMHS between 1996/97 and 1997/98, these increases were counter-balanced by other trusts showing reductions [**EXHIBIT 13**]. There was no apparent regional pattern – a London trust was as likely as a Newcastle trust to show a growth or a fall.

35. Without better figures, it is difficult to assess how significant changes in referral patterns are, and difficult to reconcile the observed pattern with reported pressures. It is plausible that more general increases were experienced in 1998/99 and 1999/2000 after the data for the Exhibit were collected, but other explanations exist – for example:

- those trusts with good data systems are also those trusts that have developed links with primary care services to help relieve demands;

- while there is little overall increase in the number of children being referred to CAMHS, the complexity of cases is increasing; and/or

- high staff vacancy rates in some CAMHS and in some regions are placing strain on the fewer staff available to support the children.

Health authorities should be monitoring demand as part of their assessment of the level of resources needed, and should evaluate the cause and extent of any fluctuations in demand. In all likelihood, the figures reflect trusts' abilities to respond, rather than the 'actual' demand for their services.

EXHIBIT 13

Changes in numbers of referral between 1996/97 and 1997/98

Some trusts experienced significant increase in demand, but these were counter-balanced by other trusts showing a reduction.

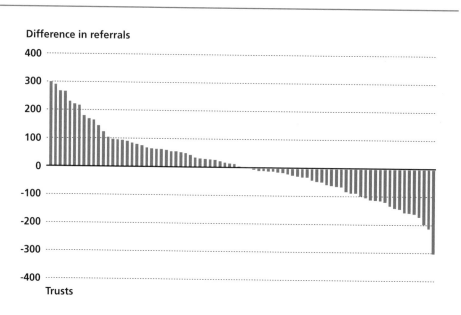

Difference in referrals

Trusts

Source: Audit Commission trust questionnaires

36. Whatever the local trends in demand, and explanation of the cause, some health authorities spent more than others on meeting demand through services delivered as 'extra-contractual referrals' (ECRs).[1] The amount, and the percentage of the total specialist CAMHS budget spent on ECRs, varied considerably [EXHIBIT 14] and almost one-quarter of health authorities spent 20 per cent or more of their CAMHS budget in this way. A high use of ECRs and low use of contracts may have indicated poor control by a health authority of the services that it was purchasing.

37. However, care is needed when interpreting these figures. Sometimes ECRs provided a valuable flexibility for children and young people whose problems required a level or type of service for which the health authority had no contract. Conversely, some health authorities with low ECR rates required admission to inappropriate services where they had contracts, rather than allow children to be referred more appropriately to more specialised but more distant services. Now that ECRs are no longer available, authorities need to ensure that they balance good financial control with sufficient flexibility to respond appropriately to the highly specialised needs of some young people.

---

[1] 'Contract' terminology was current at the start of the local audits and was used in most of the audit documentation. Although the term 'service agreement' is now preferred and generally adopted – because it is shorter and more widely understood – the term 'contract' has been used throughout this report. The term 'ECR' related to work commissioned for which there was no formal pre-existing contract or specification or understanding of how the work would be delivered. ECRs were often used for highly specialised services, delivered at some distance from the child's home or health authority.

EXHIBIT 14

Extra-contractual referrals

Almost one-quarter of health authorities spent 20 per cent or more of their budget in this way.

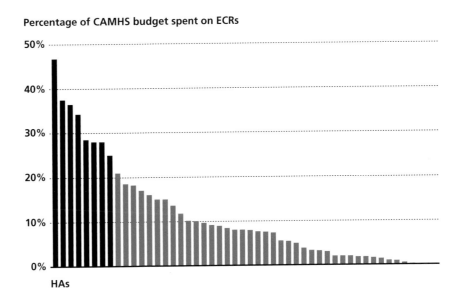

Percentage of CAMHS budget spent on ECRs

HAs

Source: Audit Commission health authority questionnaires

38. One option is to commission the highly specialised services jointly with other health authorities. This is an effective method of handling low and unpredictable demand (Ref. 48). With NHS inpatient care, the numbers of children are such that it is almost inevitable that a unit will need to be funded by several health authorities (Ref. 49). However, the audits indicated that only two in five health authorities were co-operating to agree specifications for this type of provision. This lack of co-ordination causes frustration for the trust providing the service, and confusion for other trusts wishing to refer children to it. Health authorities that are not already doing so should be drawing up arrangements for joint commissioning with others to make sure that they can provide for all the needs of children and young people in their areas, while maintaining financial control and ensuring the viability and quality of specialist centres.

Variations in staffing

39. As well as variations in resources, the audits also found that trusts varied substantially in the level and mix of staff they deploy. All trusts audited by the Commission provided community-based CAMHS services.[I] Some trusts also provided day-patient and inpatient services [TABLE 3]; the audit found that staff resources were greater in these trusts [EXHIBIT 15].

40. Half of the trusts that provided only community services had fewer than 11 full-time equivalent staff[II] and many had just a handful. The handbook produced jointly by the DoH and DfE (Ref. 17) expressed concern about small teams:

> *The size of team will depend upon its range of responsibilities and tasks. There is no single formula for the appropriate size of a team, but there is a size below which the service's viability is called into question. Professional isolation should be avoided.*

I   The report uses the term 'community' principally to cover work carried out in clinics. Some of these clinics may be on hospital sites, others may be elsewhere – such as in GP practices. In these cases, children visit the clinician. Other aspects of community services involve clinicians visiting schools, social services premises, and children in their own homes.

II   Full-time equivalent (FTE) has the same meaning as whole-time equivalent (WTE).

TABLE 3

The mix of services available

	Community services only	Community services and day services	Community services and inpatient services	Community services, day services and inpatient services	Total
Number of trusts	67	15	11	31	**124**
Percentage	54	12	9	25	**100**

Source: Audit Commission trust questionnaires database

EXHIBIT 15

Staff numbers in trusts that provide specialist CAMHS

Trusts vary considerably in their staffing resources – with greater resources available in those that provide day-patient and inpatient services.

Number of FTE staff in the CAMHS

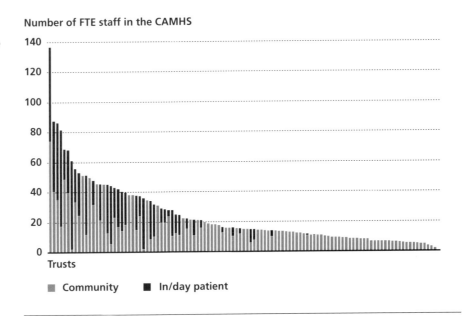

Trusts

■ Community ■ In/day patient

Source: Audit Commission trust questionnaire database

41. A wide range of professionals work in specialist CAMHS [EXHIBIT 16], although the mix of disciplines varied widely in different trusts [EXHIBIT 17, overleaf]. Individual trusts had very different mixes of staff and some disciplines were represented more widely than others [EXHIBIT 18, overleaf].

EXHIBIT 16

The proportional make-up of professional staffing in specialist CAMHS

A wide range of professionals work in specialist CAMHS.

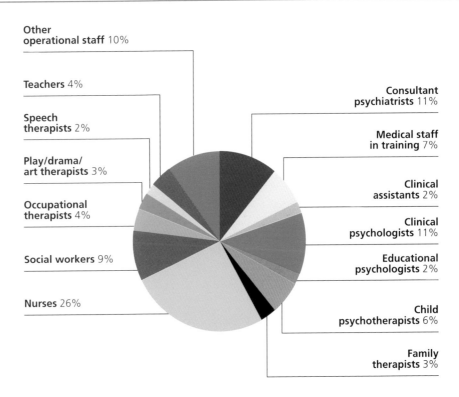

Other operational staff 10%

Teachers 4%

Speech therapists 2%

Play/drama/ art therapists 3%

Occupational therapists 4%

Social workers 9%

Nurses 26%

Consultant psychiatrists 11%

Medical staff in training 7%

Clinical assistants 2%

Clinical psychologists 11%

Educational psychologists 2%

Child psychotherapists 6%

Family therapists 3%

Source: Audit Commission trust questionnaire database – full-time equivalent staff numbers

EXHIBIT 17

Professionals working in specialist community CAMHS

There is wide variation in the mix of professionals working in community CAMHS...

Number of FTE operational staff in the CAMHS

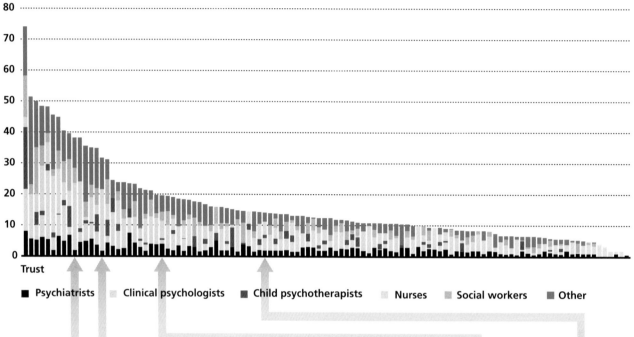

...each trust has a different composition and combination of staff disciplines.

Staff discipline	South coast	East Anglia	North West	South West
Child and adolescent psychiatry	4.5	4.5	4.0	3.0
Clinical assistants and staff in training	3.5	1.0	0.3	0.5
Clinical psychology	3.3	2.0	1.2	2.5
Child psychotherapy	1.1	5.3	0.6	0
Family therapy	1.2	1.0	0	0
Psychiatric nursing	15.1	0	5.1	3.0
Other nursing	0	5.0	0.5	0
Social work	0	8.0	3.0	3.7
Educational psychology	0	1.5	0	0
Occupational therapy	0	0	0.9	0
Play and drama therapy	2.8	2.0	0	0
Other disciplines	6.7	1.0	4.0	0
Total staff – operational	38.2	31.3	19.6	12.7
Total staff – administrative	9.8	9.2	8.4	5.8
Total staff	48.0	40.5	28.0	18.5

Source: Audit Commission trust questionnaire database – full-time equivalent staff numbers

EXHIBIT 18

Staff disciplines within community CAMHS trusts

Some disciplines are better represented in services than others.

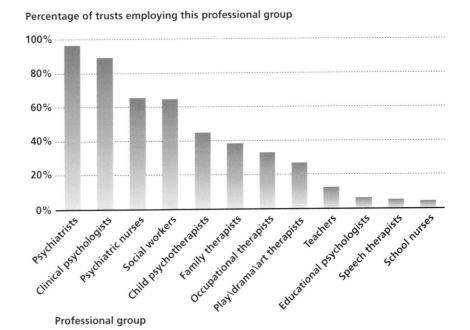

Percentage of trusts employing this professional group

Professional group

Source: Audit Commission trust questionnaire database – full-time equivalent staff numbers

42. As with overall resources, this variation does not represent any systematic response to needs. For example, the audit identified that almost 120 posts for child psychotherapists existed in the audited trusts in England and Wales, but that these posts were not evenly distributed across England and Wales. Almost half the child psychotherapy posts are in the London NHS region. In contrast, very few opportunities exist for child psychotherapists to work north of Birmingham [**EXHIBIT 19**]. One reason that most child psychotherapists are employed in the south of England is that for many years almost all child psychotherapy training centres were based in North London. Only recently have training courses for these specialists been set up in other parts of the country. Because some disciplines are better represented in some local services than others, it is probable that some trusts do not have access to the full range of skills currently regarded as necessary for the satisfactory delivery of specialist CAMHS (Ref. 17).

Vacancies

43. Some imbalances may be caused by difficulties in recruiting suitable staff. The audit collected details of staffing establishments and vacancies for each of the trusts. The audit classified a post as vacant if it had remained unfilled for three months or more. Vacancies were analysed by profession and region; a national summary reveals some regions with difficulties – particularly London [**TABLE 4**].

EXHIBIT 19

Deployment of child psychotherapists

More psychotherapist support is available to children in the south of England than elsewhere.

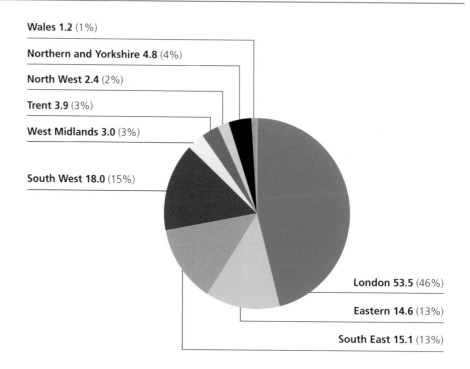

Wales **1.2** (1%)

Northern and Yorkshire **4.8** (4%)

North West **2.4** (2%)

Trent **3.9** (3%)

West Midlands **3.0** (3%)

South West **18.0** (15%)

London **53.5** (46%)

Eastern **14.6** (13%)

South East **15.1** (13%)

Source: Audit Commission trust questionnaire database – full-time equivalent staff numbers

TABLE 4

Vacancy levels

Vacancies were analysed by profession and region, and a national summary reveals some regions with difficulties – particularly London.

	London	Eastern	Northern and Yorkshire	North West	South East	South and West	Trent	West Midlands	Wales	Total
Est. (FTE) psychiatrists	37.5	32.4	41.8	37.2	35.8	43.6	18.4	13.8	14.8	**275.3**
Vacant posts (FTE) psychiatrists	11.5	2.6	4.9	3.0	2.9	4.0	0.2	3.5	2.9	**35.5**
Percentage vacancy	*30.6*	*8.1*	*11.7*	*8.1*	*8.0*	*9.2*	*1.0*	*25.4*	*19.6*	***12.9***
Est. (FTE) clinical psychologists	59.3	23.1	50.3	39.1	28.5	42.4	17.2	17.9	10.3	**288.1**
Vacant posts (FTE) clinical psychologists	16.2	2.9	5.2	5.1	5.6	4.3	2.5	3.0	0.4	**45.2**
Percentage vacancy	*27.3*	*12.5*	*10.3*	*13.0*	*19.6*	*10.1*	*14.6*	*16.8*	*3.9*	***15.7***
Est. (FTE) child psychotherapists	53.5	14.6	4.8	2.4	15.1	18.8	3.9	3.0	1.2	**117.3**
Vacant posts (FTE) child psychotherapists	20.3	0.0	0.0	0.0	0.5	0.0	0.0	0.0	0.7	**21.5**
Percentage vacancy	*37.9*	*0.0*	*0.0*	*0.0*	*3.3*	*0.0*	*0.0*	*0.0*	*58.3*	***18.3***
Est. (FTE) CPN	11.2	25.3	50.1	51.8	26.9	65.3	15.5	13.8	2.0	**261.7**
Vacant posts (FTE) CPN	0.0	0.0	1.0	0.0	0.2	4.0	4.1	3.0	0.0	**12.3**
Percentage vacancy	*0.0*	*0.0*	*2.0*	*0.0*	*0.7*	*6.1*	*26.5*	*21.8*	*0.0*	***4.7***
Est. (FTE) social workers	39.3	31.9	27.8	26.8	38.9	29.4	9.1	9.0	18.0	**230.2**
Vacant posts (FTE) social workers	15.0	0.5	2.0	1.5	1.8	3.7	0.0	1.5	0.0	**26.0**
Percentage vacancy	*38.2*	*1.6*	*7.2*	*5.6*	*4.6*	*12.6*	*0.0*	*8.3*	*0.0*	***11.3***

Source: Audit Commission trust database

Referrals and working patterns

44. Children with similar problems were seen by different professions in different trusts. In some cases, this may have been because they required intervention from different members of a multidisciplinary team. But referrals may sometimes be allocated on the basis of which professional had time available, rather than on their particular set of skills.

45. Yet different professionals work in different ways; and they vary in how often they see individual children [EXHIBIT 20]. Most children and young people seen during the sample four-week period of the audit were seen again within four weeks – 40 per cent within two weeks, and 18 per cent within a week. But psychotherapists saw 40 per cent of children within a week – four times the rate of psychiatrists or psychologists.

46. The length of time for which children received treatment also differed depending on which profession was treating them. About two-thirds of the children discharged from CAMHS during the sample month had been in the system for less than six months, although one in every sixth child discharged had been in the system for over two years [EXHIBIT 21]. Psychotherapists were more than twice as likely as psychologists to work with children for over two years [EXHIBIT 22], and half as likely to discharge them in under one month. This variation is understandable given the particular therapeutic approach adopted by psychotherapists.

47. Given the differing skills and therapeutic methods of different professionals, trusts must ask themselves why they have such different combinations of staff. The 1993/94 review of CAMHS (Ref. 21) found that the numbers and distribution of staff in specialist CAMHS were not based on assessed needs, but were largely the result of historical service patterns. This feature still seems to apply. Only just over one-third of trusts (38 per cent) reported having a written operational policy on the roles, professional relationships and responsibilities of the different professionals involved in CAMHS.

EXHIBIT 20

Contact frequency by professional group

Psychotherapists were four times more likely to see a child again within a week than either psychiatrists or psychologists.

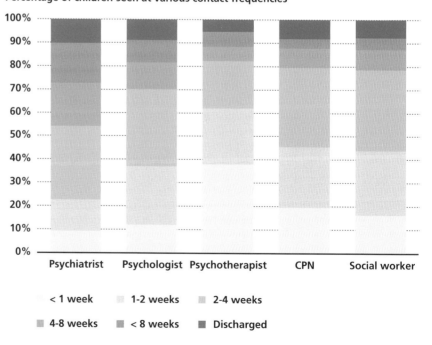

Percentage of children seen at various contact frequencies

	< 1 week	1-2 weeks	2-4 weeks
	4-8 weeks	< 8 weeks	Discharged

Source: Audit Commission case characteristics database

EXHIBIT 21

The length of treatment periods for children and young people in CAMHS

About two-thirds of the children are in the system for under six months.

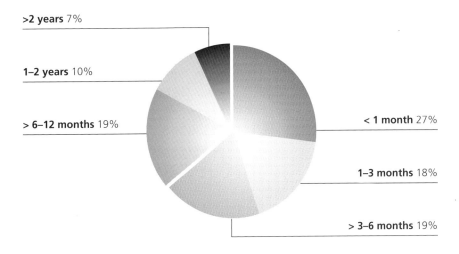

>2 years 7%

1–2 years 10%

> 6–12 months 19%

< 1 month 27%

1–3 months 18%

> 3–6 months 19%

Source: Audit Commission case characteristics database

EXHIBIT 22

Length of treatment periods of different professional groups

A psychotherapist is twice as likely as a psychologist to treat a child for over two years.

Percentage of children seen

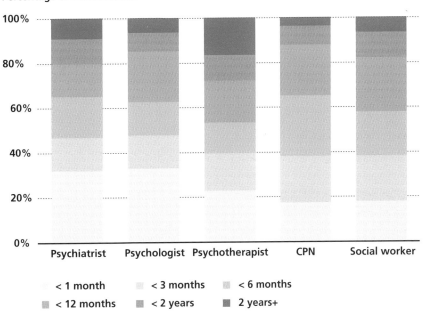

< 1 month	< 3 months	< 6 months
< 12 months	< 2 years	2 years+

Source: Audit Commission case characteristics database

48. Trusts should first review with their commissioners what needs they are being asked to meet. They should then consider the numbers and type of staff that they employ and the skills that they bring to bear, to see how well these match the problems that they are being asked to tackle. For some types of staff, information describing the service and explaining roles is available. For example, the Child Psychotherapy Trust is actively promoting better integration and distribution of psychotherapy within multidisciplinary teams (Refs. 50, 51 and 52). A radical option adopted by one trust is to acknowledge the inevitable overlap in the skills offered by CAMHS professionals, and to create a team of generic workers [CASE STUDY 1]. Whether trusts take this route, or continue with an existing framework of differing professional groups, many CAMHS providers must still work out how to adjust and train[I] their staffing establishment to match the needs of the children whom they see, and of their referrers.

[I]   The audits showed that only 54 of 124 trusts (44 per cent) had a designated staff training budget for CAMHS.

CASE STUDY 1

Royal Liverpool Children's NHS Trust – generic workers

The Royal Liverpool Children's Hospital NHS Trust (Alder Hey) has set-up a system of graded mental health practitioners (MHPs).

Grade 1 MHPs are members of the CAMHS teams working at Tier 2 and Tier 3. At this level, the main function is to carry out assessments and therapeutic work, and to adopt the case manager role in a proportion of cases (those that are routine and less complex). Their overall level of responsibility increases over time; at the top of the 'ladder', Grade 1 MHPs are responsible for supervising the majority of their child cases, and the work of some other professionals.

Professionals appointed at Grade 1 will have had relatively limited experience in community child mental health, but probably more extensive experience in a related area, such as child nursing or working with families in an adult mental health setting. Grade 1 MHPs hold a recognised health or social work qualification.

At MHP Grade 2, practitioners take clinical responsibility for a wide range of clinical problems, particularly the more complex and severe cases. They are expected to work within complex professional networks and to relate their work to relevant clinical research. They will have gained experience of a wide range of clinical problems, and will be able to weigh up the relative merits of different treatment approaches. They are appointed on the basis that they have the skills and aptitude to co-ordinate other members of the team.

Professionals appointed at Grade 2 will normally have at least five years' experience in their own profession, and in a community/outpatient child mental health service. They will have completed a substantial proportion of a recognised training course in a specific area of clinical practice, such as cognitive behavioural therapy or family therapy, leading to UKCP registration or another equivalent national standard.

1999 Salaries

MHP Grade 1:	£16,268 to £22,775
MHP Grade 2:	£25,038 to £31,569

Links with other agencies

Arrangements to support Tier 1 and other providers

49. Specialist CAMHS must also work closely with other service providers. The NHS Health Advisory Service report, *Together We Stand* (Ref. 1), recommended that CAMHS should provide consultation and advice to help staff in other services to manage children with milder problems and to refer appropriately to specialist services. The diaries showed that, over all trusts, CAMHS professionals spent, on average, only 2 per cent of their time providing consultation to others, and that the important task of supporting Tier 1 services accounted for only 1 per cent of their time [EXHIBIT 23].

EXHIBIT 23

Time spent on different activities by CAMHS staff

Only 1 per cent of specialist staff time is spent providing support to Tier 1 services.

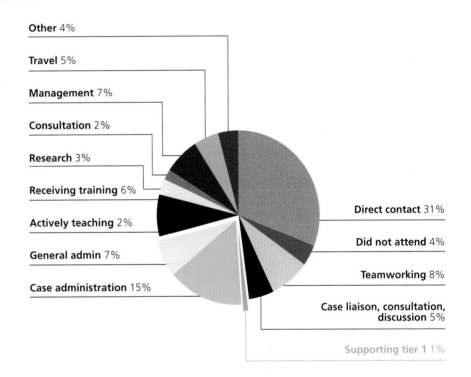

Source: Audit Commission diary database

The increasing emphasis on prevention and early intervention will make the training and support of Tier 1 workers by specialist CAMHS staff essential, and health authorities should require trusts operating CAMHS to support these staff

50. Little improvement in the support to Tier 1 services can be expected until health authorities make this type of work a requirement in their contracts and service agreements. At present, some health authorities (albeit a minority) do not monitor any of the services delivered by trusts; those that do usually rely on the number of face-to-face contacts. As long as the number of face-to-face contacts is used as the sole contract currency to measure performance, trust staff will understandably concentrate on working *directly* with the children and young people referred to them. But the increasing emphasis on prevention and early intervention will make the training and support of Tier 1 workers by specialist CAMHS staff essential, and health authorities should require trusts operating CAMHS to support these staff. One early estimate was that this might require about 10 per cent of staff time [**CASE STUDY 2**].

CASE STUDY 2

Support for Tier 1

Extract from a paper written in 1993 by Eva Holmes, Principal Officer, Enfield Child and Family Service

A significant proportion of the work of the service is spent in planned regular consultation work with other professional groups outside the service. These are groups of staff who work with children and have concerns about mental health problems in their work. Consultation enables us to help identify complex cases requiring direct treatment for the child and family service and to offer adequate support so that the less difficult cases can be managed at the primary care level. In addition to regular consultation usually weekly or fortnightly to special schools and units, 'ad hoc' consultation to GPs, social workers, educational psychologists and paediatricians over particular cases also occurs.

It is estimated that this work, together with attendance at planning and policy groups, takes about 10 per cent of staff time and provides a valuable preventive and supportive function, given the high number of children with emotional problems in the community. A more sophisticated recording system is being considered to monitor this work more accurately.

51. Another way of helping Tier 1 is to employ link workers. A number of trusts are doing this to promote better inter-agency working, and ultimately to reduce the level of referrals to the specialist services [CASE STUDY 3]. For instance, Southern Derbyshire Mental Health Trust uses a 'locality worker', who is funded by the Southern Derbyshire Health Authority, to provide advice to primary care workers and to take direct referrals. By dealing with potentially inappropriate referrals and supporting other professionals in their work, this post is believed to have significantly reduced the demand on CAMHS and the waiting times.[1]

---

[1] The auditor concerned has recommended that the trust further evaluate the impact of the post.

CASE STUDY 3

Links between specialist CAMHS and others

Lincolnshire District Healthcare Trust

Lincolnshire has used health authority funding to increase its general nursing establishment, freeing up five community psychiatric nurses (CPNs). These CPNs now spend half a day every week providing a service to children in the residential homes managed by Lincolnshire Social Services. More generally, the same CPNs are developing informal links with other disciplines, and the Trust is now able to offer the residential homes direct access to the full range of its multidisciplinary expertise.

Bassetlaw Trust (Nottinghamshire)

Bassetlaw has established school liaison meetings with special schools in its area and most of the comprehensive schools. These meetings provide an opportunity for schools to raise concerns about children who may be exhibiting behavioural problems at school. Some children may subsequently be referred to the CAMHS team, but the experience in Bassetlaw suggests that providing this sort of liaison service has actually prevented referrals rather than increased them.

North East Wales NHS Trust

A primary care project was set up in 1996 in the Connah's Quay area of Flintshire by the former Clwydian Community Care NHS Trust to tackle, in some depth, the needs of children under the age of eight. The exercise started with a full needs assessment in the area, which included asking a cross-section of parents about their perceptions of need and how they thought these might be measured. It also involved talking with primary care professionals about what could be done to address needs, and to identify specific training and support requirements. The project culminated in the design of a mental health screening method that was acceptable to both parents and non-specialist professionals.

(continued overleaf)

CASE STUDY 3 (continued)

Throughout, the project team was sensitive to the concerns of parents and the need to build trust between parents and professionals, and also to the need to create good working relationships between primary healthcare staff operating at Tier 1 and specialist CAMHS staff working in other tiers.

The project in Connah's Quay offers help in three specific ways:

- by giving brief and practical psychological help to families at early stages in the development of problems – by non-specialists and specialists – in both family counselling and school settings;

- by providing teachers with information and consultation opportunities so that they can understand their own impact on classes; and

- by offering parenting workshops for the parents of all children in nursery education and in the reception year in school – in large part to address low parenting confidence which is manifested as expressions of concern about child behaviour.

The project is now fully underway and being closely reviewed. It will be completed and the results published, in March 2000.

52. To be most effective, CAMHS staff need to network widely within the health, education and social care sectors. Auditors asked trusts specifically about their working arrangements with all other agencies and sectors where strong parallel commitments to the welfare of children might be expected [TABLE 5].

53. The results suggest that 56 per cent of CAMHS operated formal contracts with GPs at the time of the audit, and that a large number had delivered training to GPs. However, about one-quarter of trusts delivering CAMHS had no real liaison or joint working with GPs. Working relationships with the youth justice services (which have responsibility for managing many of the same clients, especially during adolescence) were much weaker. In this area, over one-third of CAMHS trusts said that joint working with youth justice services was inadequate. Equally, two-thirds of managers of youth justice services reported problems gaining access to mental health services (Ref. 53).

TABLE 5

Percentage of CAMHS working with others

	Formal contract	Member of planning forum	Trained by CAMHS	No real liaison or joint working
GPs	56	34	47	23
Community nurses/HVs	35	36	76	16
School health service	35	44	68	17
Paediatricians	44	54	58	15
Adult MH services	35	37	39	25
Drug and alcohol services	29	33	27	37
Learning disability services	33	37	34	27
Children's social workers	45	52	47	17
Youth justice services	27	35	27	35
Special educational needs service	34	44	39	21
Educational psychology service	35	44	30	22
LEA schools	30	27	30	23
Independent and GMS	30	25	21	30
EDB and special schools	32	29	27	24

Source: Audit Commission trust questionnaire database

The level of administrative work

54. Better liaison with others will take more time. It may be possible to release time by improving the support that professionals receive. It appears that the amount of time professionals spent on administration is considerable; this accounted for almost one-quarter (22 per cent) of their time (Exhibit 23, page 37). It is important that all trusts look at administration from first principles – to check that all the forms being completed are necessary, useful, and not being duplicated within the team, and that all the administrative tasks are being performed by the right people. If administrative processes are not already streamlined, reducing bureaucracy is one way of releasing staff time.

55. Case-related administration may be considerable in complex inter-agency cases, and it may be necessary for the supervising professional to take on this work. If a local review confirms that the tasks are indeed necessary, it might still be possible to release time by increasing the levels of administrative support in CAMHS. It might also suggest an increased role for new technology, such as the use of e-mail and intranet systems.

Increasing the use of computers is not likely, in itself, to reduce the clerical and administrative burden, but it could speed things up and produce better data for communication and audit purposes. A degree of administrative overhead on professional staff is inevitable, but trusts can seek to maximise their returns from their efforts in this area, rather than simply assume that administration is a costly and inevitable burden on a professional service.

Variations in access to service-users

56. The audits showed that CAMHS varied in how accessible they were to children and young people. In some situations, access could be gained easily; in others it could be poor.

Referral routes

57. Staff in other services need to be able to call on specialist CAMHS when necessary. In practice, NHS clinicians provide the main referral route to the specialist CAMHS. The audit found that more than half the CAMHS referrals came from GPs (52 per cent), with a further 15 per cent coming from paediatricians. Only 14 per cent came directly from social services and education combined [EXHIBIT 24], although there was significant variation in patterns between trusts [EXHIBIT 25].

58. While some CAMHS encourage referrals from social workers (see Exhibit 25), anecdotal evidence suggests that social workers make few referrals in some places because they are concerned:

- first, that the child will have to wait a long time for an appointment; and

- second, that the child will be seen in a health service clinic, rather than in a setting that he or she is used to and may find more acceptable.

EXHIBIT 24

Sources of referral to specialist community CAMHS

Only 14 per cent of referrals were from social services or education.

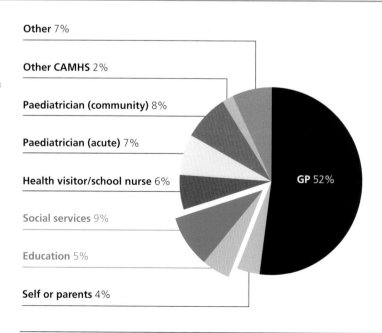

Other 7%

Other CAMHS 2%

Paediatrician (community) 8%

Paediatrician (acute) 7%

Health visitor/school nurse 6%

Social services 9%

Education 5%

Self or parents 4%

GP 52%

Source: Audit Commission case characteristics database

EXHIBIT 25

Sources of referral to specialist community CAMHS

There was considerable variation in the level of referrals from social services departments.

Source: Audit Commission case characteristics database

Percentage of referrals

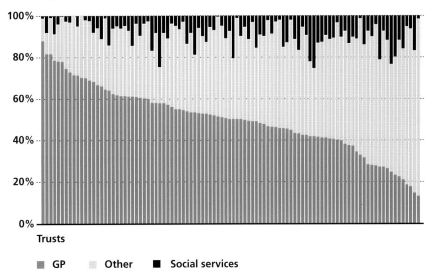

Trauma

Trusts

■ GP ▦ Other ■ Social services

59. Conversely, some CAMHS require referrals to be routed through a GP, so as to reduce unsuitable referrals. Specialist staff can spend a lot of time on children who are referred to them inappropriately. But rigid restrictions on access may create inequity. It may also frustrate non-medical, but specialist, mental health professionals.[I]

60. There is no 'best answer' as to how to manage this interface. Each CAMHS needs to think carefully about how it sets its 'entrance requirements'. One approach is to develop a 'named list' of professionals in addition to GPs who may make direct referrals to specialist CAMHS. Admission to the list would require meetings and discussion with the specialist team. Dialogue between the specialists and those making referrals would lead to improvement in the suitability of referrals.

I   Educational psychologists are in this category. They spend much of their time working with children with psychological problems that affect their schooling, and are usually aware of what could be done by CAMHS to help, but in some trusts educational psychologists are not able to make a referral to CAMHS without a 'medical authorisation' from the child's GP.

61. An alternative approach is to set clear protocols describing *which*, *when* and *how* children and young people should be referred to specialist CAMHS. These protocols should be developed by providers working with commissioners as part of the commissioning process; the expected numbers of referrals should be estimated and taken into account when setting the budget. A systematic approach such as this could help, given the growing complexity of the commissioning process with the introduction of primary care groups in England and local health groups in Wales. Different trusts are adopting different approaches from the highly systematic in Doncaster [CASE STUDY 4] to an 'open door' policy exemplified by Bassetlaw Trust for young adult referrals:

> *Contacting the Team – we accept self-referrals, referrals from GPs and voluntary and statutory agencies. Please telephone or write for a referral form or for further information to: Young Adult Service, Retford Hospital.*
> *Source: Bassetlaw 'Young Adult Service' publicity leaflet.*

CASE STUDY 4

A systematic approach to referral – Doncaster

A new strategy has been agreed and issued by Doncaster Health Authority, Combined Children's Services, Education and Social Services Directorates of Doncaster Metropolitan Council and the Child and Family Mental Health Service.

The joint strategy defines mental health problems as including:
Emotional, behavioural and social relationship difficulties/disturbance, sufficiently marked or prolonged to cause suffering or risk to the full development of the child or young person and also distress or cause disturbance to the family or community.

At particular risk are those:

- At risk of abuse
- Looked after by the local authority
- With chronic illness, physical and/or learning disability or delay
- Whose parents suffer from mental health problems or physical illness, where social, educational, health and economic pressures affect their lives
- With disruptive attachments and/or losses.

A system of service response has been agreed which categorises problems into four levels.

The levels depend on:

- The severity of the problem
- The persistence of the problem
- The amount of support and degree of expertise that is needed to help.

A system for co-operation and joint working between the levels has been defined.

Guidance and protocols have been produced for different agencies on the procedures for referring to the specialist child and family mental health service. The following is that for **education**.

1. Problem identified.

2. Consideration is given to the level of intervention required, possibly accessing consultancy arrangements with child and family mental health service.

3. Once a decision has been made that a problem is of a severity which warrants a Level 3 response, then a referral is made using the appropriate referral form. The referral **must include**:

   - previous help and input to the child and/or family from professionals working at Level 1 and 2; and
   - the views of the educational psychologist.

   A copy of the referral should also be sent to the child's GP with a pro-forma letter inviting him/her to send any relevant medical information to the child and family mental health team.

4. The school or referring agency will also contribute to the assessment and review.

Waiting times

62. Waiting times for assessment or treatment are important in many services, but for children, a long wait can be particularly detrimental. Although a growing demand for CAMHS could be expected to increase the length of time that children have to wait, a number of local audit reports have shown that the connection is not a simple one: some trusts have always had long waiting times, while others have a record of seeing children more quickly.

63. From the trust questionnaires, the median waiting time from referral to first appointment for non-urgent cases was found to be between ten and fifteen weeks **[EXHIBIT 26]**. Some trusts said that they did not operate a waiting list; any child would be seen as soon as he or she was able to attend. At the other extreme, about 10 per cent of trusts could not offer an appointment within six months, and in at least five CAMHS the average wait for an assessment was more than a year. Auditors also found great variability within individual CAMHS. In over one-third of the trusts audited, the waiting time for a CAMHS appointment in one part of the service was at least twice as long as the CAMHS average within the same trust.

64. The local audits showed that about three out of every five health authorities had agreed maximum waiting times for routine referrals with their service providers. All should be setting such standards.

EXHIBIT 26

Waiting times for a non-urgent first CAMHS appointment

About 10 per cent of trusts could not offer an appointment within six months.

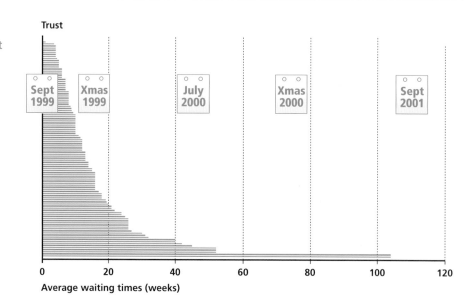

Trust

| Sept 1999 | Xmas 1999 | July 2000 | Xmas 2000 | Sept 2001 |

Average waiting times (weeks)

Source: Audit Commission trust questionnaire database

Over one-third of trusts felt that they could not respond effectively to young people presenting in a crisis

Arrangements for emergency and 24-hour cover

65. Arrangements for emergency and 24-hour cover are an essential element in a good quality service. Exactly one-half (50 per cent) of health authorities surveyed said that they had agreed arrangements for emergency and 24-hour cover with their providers.

66. There are a number of different ways to arrange suitable emergency care for young people who present with mental health problems. Some trusts deliberately minimise the need for activity out of hours by CAMHS professionals, providing cover in other ways [CASE STUDY 5]. In Liverpool, children who deliberately self-harm are not admitted by CAMHS out of hours, but are seen instead by paediatricians and admitted to paediatric wards. They are assessed by CAMHS professionals on the following morning when full professional networks are available. An out-of-hours service is provided by child psychiatrists for those children who present (relatively infrequently) with psychiatric emergencies, such as psychosis and severe depression. However, over one-third of trusts felt that they could not respond effectively to young people presenting in a crisis. All health authorities should review their own arrangements to ensure adequate local emergency cover.

CASE STUDY 5

Providing 24-hour cover – Gwent NHS Healthcare Trust

The Gwent Health Authority has a contract that is administered and monitored on its behalf by the staff of the specialist CAMHS service to admit adolescents in need to the adolescent psychiatric unit in Cardiff. As this inpatient unit does not take emergency admissions, the specialist service in Gwent also has an arrangement to admit certain adolescents for short periods to a new mental illness unit for adults. There is a comprehensive package of arrangements between the two services based on an agreed protocol to support this work. Also, the paediatric services will admit children and younger adolescents in emergencies when this is necessary.

'Did not attend' rates

67. A high incidence of missed appointments (DNAs or 'did not attend') may indicate problems with access and acceptability, or the appropriateness of the referral (Ref. 54). DNA rates may increase if:

- clinics are sited inconveniently far from localities where needs are high;

- the service does not offer an appointment in a child's home, school, GP surgery or in a voluntary agency setting;

- the waiting time is too long; and/or

- clinic settings are not child- or parent-friendly and more than half of CAMHS trusts identified accommodation as a 'major problem' **[EXHIBIT 27]**.

68. Many CAMHS have a 'bad accommodation tale' to tell. For example, one northern trust expects part-time professionals to interview children in a shared office. This means that busy staff have to stagger child appointments and their use of the office so that each child can be given the appropriate privacy. In a trust in the south west, the interview room for adolescents is located adjacent to a child hearing clinic!

69. However, high DNA rates may not be due to problems over accommodation but may result from difficulties over referrals. The ideas already proposed for improving referral routes – especially for better briefing of referrers – can help **[CASE STUDY 6]**.

EXHIBIT 27

Problems identified by trusts

More than half of the CAMHS trusts identified accommodation as a 'major problem'.

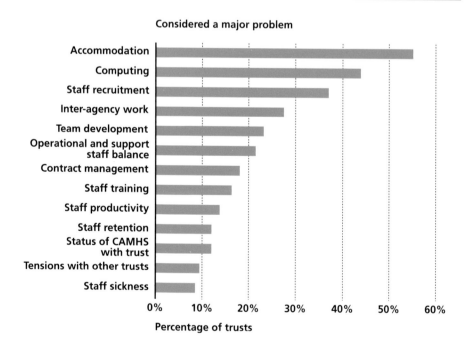

Considered a major problem

Accommodation
Computing
Staff recruitment
Inter-agency work
Team development
Operational and support staff balance
Contract management
Staff training
Staff productivity
Staff retention
Status of CAMHS with trust
Tensions with other trusts
Staff sickness

0% 10% 20% 30% 40% 50% 60%

Percentage of trusts

Source: Audit Commission trust questionnaire database

CASE STUDY 6

Reducing DNA rates

Gwent Healthcare NHS Trust

Gwent undertook a review of patterns of non-attendance, and found a DNA rate for the service overall of 22 per cent. The service has many sites conveniently located for the main centres of population and transport; service location was not found to be the main causes of a failure to attend. Instead, the review found a complex web of factors, with referrers experiencing many difficulties.

Referrers often failed to gain the active co-operation of families, and instead assumed a passive acceptance and compliance with their recommendations. There were also misunderstandings about the actual role, nature, capabilities and capacity of the specialist service. A high turnover of staff in some referring agencies resulted in inexperienced staff not following appropriate procedures. Referring agencies also sometimes closed cases while the referral was still being processed.

Sometimes low attendance rates were the result of an inappropriate referral in the first place. People were referred who exhibited 'worrying patterns of behaviour', even though referrers considered psychiatric disorder and the consequent need for specialist

healthcare to be a low possibility. In part, referrals of this type are intended to share anxiety about the situation; but they also revealed some gaps in referrers' interview skills and knowledge about the symptoms and signs of more serious disorders. Inappropriate referrals to CAMHS could also be traced to gaps in the overall pattern of services available, where the ability of other agencies to offer preventive and therapeutic services had been reduced. Many specialist services are being pressed by rising demand and from the tenets of evidence-based practice to concentrate on a core business around identifiable and treatable disorders.

This work so far suggests that referrals should be better prepared and that family members should also be better prepared for referral. More time and better consultation about cases between potential referrers and staff of specialist CAMHS could improve mutual satisfaction with the process, result in other methods of intervention, achieve higher rates of compliance and reduce inappropriate referrals.

A computer-based clinical recording system is now being used to study the referral process and DNA rates, and to track cases through the specialist CAMHS system from first contact to closure.

Outer London

A CAMHS team in one outer London trust suffered a 38 per cent DNA rate for first referrals. The problem was caused partly by poorly prepared referrals. GPs, in particular, and some school doctors, were not aware of the services offered by the team, and consequently could not explain to parents what treatment was involved. Other factors in the high DNA rate were transport difficulties and low literacy levels. A DNA audit was recently carried out within the Trust, and the team concerned has started to hold seminars with GPs to promote awareness of the service offered by its Tier 3 clinic, and to encourage more appropriate referrals to other providers. In addition, the team now telephones and sends reminders to children prior to their visit.

Surrey Oaklands NHS Trust

This trust had a lower DNA rate than the national average, but a relatively high incidence of DNAs for children who were referred by health visitors. An audit project helped health visitors to make more appropriate referrals and to prepare clients better. Open days run by the service also helped to reduce the overall level of failures to attend.

Across all trusts completing the diary exercise, staff indicated that they were wasting 4 per cent of their time on DNAs

70. 'Non-attendance' disrupts staff time. More importantly, the children and families who do not attend do not receive the help on offer. Across all trusts completing the diary exercise, staff indicated that they were wasting 4 per cent of their time on DNAs (Exhibit 23, page 37). Eighty-three per cent of trusts said that they monitored their DNA rates. Only one in five said that they had a rate that was less than 15 per cent. Three-quarters of trusts had a routine procedure for following up young people who failed to meet appointments. All should have such a system, and all should be investigating the causes of DNAs, with the aim of improving access to CAMHS.

71. If targets are set to reduce DNAs, trusts must avoid introducing perverse incentives to clinicians and others involved in delivering CAMHS. No one should be penalised for including on their caseloads children and families whose attendance is likely to be poor, but whose needs are such that they stand to gain much from help from CAMHS.

Conclusion

72. Children and young people face wide variation in the services that they receive from the NHS. Resources vary by a factor of seven, and staff numbers and types vary widely. Links with other providers of services for children are often weak, and children's access to services can be highly variable. Both health authorities and trusts need to establish more consistent provision of specialist CAMHS and need to link their activities with those of other agencies. This is the subject of the next chapter.

RECOMMENDATIONS

3 A Variable Response

Health authorities and trusts should be reviewing resources. They should:

1 establish a separate budget for each CAMHS;

2 take demand into account when they assess the level and type of resources needed; and

3 take note of new arrangements (authorised in HSC 1998/198) for the joint commissioning of highly specialised services, which include those in CAMHS, to make sure that they can provide for all needs of children and young people in their areas, while maintaining financial and quality control.

Trusts should be reviewing staffing arrangements. They should:

4 pay attention to how they support their staff, particularly those with only a few staff; and

5 consider the numbers and type of staff that they employ and the skills they bring to bear, to see how well matched these are to the problems that they are being asked to tackle.

Links between specialist CAMHS and Tier 1 services should be strengthened.

6 Health authorities should require CAMHS to support Tier 1 staff.

7 Trusts should review administrative arrangements, in part to free up specialist professionals' time for support for Tier 1.

Arrangements for gaining access to CAMHS should be improved.

8 Each CAMHS needs to think carefully about how it sets its 'entrance requirements'.

9 Health authorities should set standards for maximum waiting times.

10 Health authorities should review arrangements for emergency cover with trusts to ensure adequate local arrangements.

11 Trusts should have a system for following up young people who miss appointments and should be investigating the causes in order to improve the access to CAMHS.

4

Working Together

All agencies responsible for commissioning child and adolescent mental health services must work together, with health commissioners taking the lead. All should be working to assess local needs, review services, and plan how to set priorities and to meet unmet needs. They then need to translate intentions into a strategy with service agreements that are supported by appropriate monitoring systems.

Co-ordinating the commissioning of services

73. If children and young people are to receive the help they need, the agencies responsible must commission and provide an effective range of services to help them address their problems. In particular, they must work together to ensure that their provision is well co-ordinated. Effective provision requires that services be interdependent and planned together. Research into services for children with conduct disorder shows that the costs fall across a wide range of agencies [**TABLE 6**] (Ref. 55).

74. The Government's handbook in 1995 (Ref. 17) proposed that health authorities should take the lead in commissioning mental health services for children and young people. Since then, much has changed with the introduction of primary care groups (PCGs) in England and local health groups (LHGs) in Wales. It is not yet clear what role these will take with regard to CAMHS, and how primary care trusts (PCTs) might operate is even less clear. In the immediate future, health authorities must set the strategic direction for services as part of their health improvement programmes. To do so successfully, they need to appoint a member of staff to take the lead for each area of service.

75. The audits showed that 93 per cent of health authorities have already done this for CAMHS – 5 per cent of lead officers hold posts that are at director level, 71 per cent at assistant director level and 13 per cent at section head level (with 4 per cent unspecified). The few health authorities that have not done so, should appoint a lead officer as a matter of urgency. However, one out of five (20 per cent) reported that this lead officer is not a member of an interagency group for commissioning children's services including CAMHS. For interagency work to be effective, each health authority should form a commissioning group with appropriately senior representatives from all the relevant agencies, if one does not already exist.

TABLE 6

Annual costs per child with conduct disorder (sample of ten children)
Costs are spread across a wide range of agencies.

Agency	Cost (£)
National Health Service	2,457
Local authority social services	991
Local authority education services	4,754
Voluntary sector	56
Total direct costs	**8,258**
Indirect costs (lost employment [parents], additional housework and repairs, and allowances and benefits)	7,012
Total costs	**15,270**

Source: Ref. 55

There is a real danger that specialist CAMHS, because it consumes relatively little, can be treated as trivial or irrelevant by higher spenders

76. Within such a wider group, health authority representatives may well find it difficult to raise the profile of children's mental health services with other higher-spending local authority managers. Compared with educational budgets, child and adolescent mental health services appear tiny, and it will not always be easy for health authorities to engage important partners who have other urgent agendas of their own. There is a real danger that specialist CAMHS, because it consumes relatively little, can be treated as trivial or irrelevant by higher spenders.

Agreeing the scope of services

77. Once this hurdle has been cleared, the first task facing the group is to agree a common approach. This is by no means straightforward, as different agencies – as well as different professions – use different terminologies. For example, a child psychiatrist may categorise certain symptoms in a child as 'conduct disorder'. An educational psychologist, seeing the same symptoms in a child in the classroom, may describe them primarily as 'emotional and behavioural difficulties' which, if they interfere with the child's ability to benefit from education, may be defined as 'special needs'. A social worker seeing the same child looked after by the local authority may describe him or her as having 'challenging behaviour', or express concerns about 'the emotional development of the young person'. Non-medical professions, in particular, fight shy of stigmatising a child by labelling him or her as mentally ill. One professional commented:

> *It took 18 months from starting an interagency review to agreeing to adopt the four-tier model, due to the difficulty of identifying the common values and forgetting historical problems between agencies. Once common problems were identified, an audit of each service was undertaken in a 'no blame' culture and this enabled the four-tier model to be finalised.*

78. Even within a single profession, there can be different points of view. Within child psychiatry, for example, there is a school of thought that regards much of 'conduct disorder' as a 'social' or an 'educational' problem which should be left largely to social services and/or education authorities to sort out (Ref. 56). These psychiatrists say that the label 'mental health disorder' should be restricted largely to those with genetic or organic causes that require a medically based treatment needing expertise in psychiatry.

79. Young people themselves have their own concepts of mental health and mental illness. A recent project in Scotland (Ref. 57) found that young people interviewed did not readily identify with 'mental illness'. They saw this in a traditional way, linked to the major psychotic and schizophrenic disorders of adults. Some also found it hard to recognise that the term 'mental health' might apply to themselves, but those who could were able to identify the positive signs of being mentally 'healthy' and the negative symptoms of being mentally 'unhealthy'.

Age limits in CAMHS

80. Health authorities currently commission services for different age ranges [EXHIBIT 28]. Twenty per cent of health authorities were unclear about the age range covered under their service agreements, which suggests that these have not been defined. A sizeable number commission CAMHS for those aged up to their 16th birthday only (29 per cent). This means that after 16, newly referred young people go to the adult mental health services – considered by many to be highly inappropriate, particularly where inpatient care is required (Ref. 58). And yet, the Audit Commission CAMHS databases show that 12 per cent of the young people seen were aged 16 or 17; and some were being treated by the specialist CAMHS up to the age of 25.

81. The audits even found some differences within the same trust. For example, in one CAMHS the clinical psychology service was prepared to see a child throughout his or her school years, but the child psychiatry service – operating with different protocols and constraints – stopped seeing new referrals at age 16. But by seeing a child until the end of their schooldays, even the clinical psychology service effectively withdraws its service from those aged 16 and 17 who have opted out of education. These are very often among the most vulnerable of young people. If they are managed by adult mental health services rather than CAMHS, there is a strong probability that the urgency with which they are seen – if they are seen at all – will depend on the perceived severity of their clinical illness, with less account taken of their social or psychological vulnerability.

82. All the different agencies responsible for a particular population should be clear about how the appropriate services are to be provided for children and young people of different ages, with different needs. The audits revealed the continuing problem of creating services for adolescents in many parts of England and Wales. It is particularly disappointing that, despite several specific reviews of adolescent care, services for these young people remain patchy.[I] Some services that have been specifically developed for adolescents such as the Bassetlaw Young Adult Service, and the services provided in Enfield and the Wirral, match services to needs [CASE STUDY 7, overleaf]. Although provision is influenced by age to a large extent, it is not rigidly controlled by it.

EXHIBIT 28

Age ranges specified by health authorities

Twenty-nine per cent commissioned CAMHS for those aged up to their 16th birthday only.

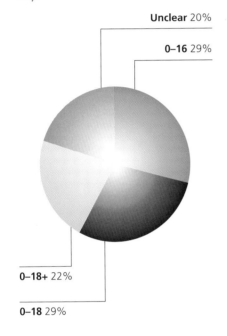

Unclear 20%

0–16 29%

0–18+ 22%

0–18 29%

Source: Audit Commission health authority questionnaire database

---

I   It is known, for example, that the peak age for children entering social services care systems is 15 years; that England and Wales has one of the highest teenage pregnancy rates in Europe; and that various local authorities have high school-exclusion rates and also high drop-out rates from education at the child's earliest opportunity. Many of these problems could, and should, appear on an adolescent mental health agenda.

CASE STUDY 7

Matching services to needs

Services for adolescents and families in Enfield (SAFE)

The service is delivered by a multidisciplinary team of mental health care professionals including a psychiatrist, clinical psychologist, child and adolescent psychotherapist, part-time educational psychologist, and two family therapists/social workers. This multidisciplinary team has been established via collaboration between:

- Enfield Community Care Trust;

- the Education Group of the Local Authority (Child Guidance); and

- Enfield Social Services.

In addition to its direct work with adolescents, the team also offers telephone and face-to-face consultations with a variety of professionals including GPs, area and residential social workers, foster parents and their link workers, school nurses and teachers.

Extract from Wirral Health Authority services specification with Wirral Community Healthcare (NHS) Trust

Services will be provided to residents of Wirral (including Neston, Parkgate and Willaston) aged 0-16 years where psychological and/or psychiatric interventions are required. Age criteria will be applied flexibly, and adolescents in the 16-19 age group will receive services for specific presenting problems where the expertise of the service can be appropriately applied, and where their level of maturity indicates appropriate referral.

Setting the agenda for joint working

83. In spite of the many difficulties, some authorities and trusts are establishing good working relations [CASE STUDY 8]. Having agreed who is to be involved in commissioning CAMHS, commissioners and service providers need to:

- assess needs systematically – consulting widely (including children and their parents) and taking a holistic approach to children's needs;

- take stock of the resources available both at Tier 1 and in specialist CAMHS at Tiers 2, 3 and 4 – checking that they have a clear picture of what is currently being spent and the quality of what is being provided; and

- transcribe needs into service requirements with priorities, identifying gaps and focusing on services of proven effectiveness. To achieve such prioritisation, some reconfiguration of services and improvement to co-operative arrangements between services may be required.

The audit findings on each of the tasks listed above are now considered in turn.

CASE STUDY 8

Co-ordinating the commissioning of services: Gwent

The specialist CAMHS in Gwent consist of five consultant-led teams and a range of more specialised services. Each of the five teams offers Tier 2 services and support to Tier 1 services as well as liaison and co-ordination with other agencies. Tier 3 services, that include separate day patient facilities for both children and adolescents as well as a range of specialist clinics, are provided at the headquarters of the service. These services are available on referral from the specialist CAMHS teams. Additionally, Tier 3 day-services are provided one day a week by staff at dispersed sites away from the base.

In April 1999, five local health groups (LHGs) were created in Gwent to commission health services. They are co-terminous with the unitary local authorities and have local authority representatives on their boards. Thus in Gwent, the LHGs, education and social services departments and specialist CAMHS teams now have areas of responsibility that are substantially co-terminous at Tiers 1 and 2.

During the last year, the staff of the various services that work with troubled children in each local authority/LHG area have been setting up CAMHS planning groups that are intending to:

- negotiate, agree, hold and develop a multi-agency, multidisciplinary approach to the delivery of services;
- provide a forum for resolving service delivery issues and problems;
- temper service provision to local need; and
- resolve contemporary problems in delivering services to particularly challenging children, young people and their families.

The intention is that each of the five CAMHS planning groups should report to a Gwent-wide committee sponsored and chaired by the Gwent Health Authority and composed of senior staff from each of the major agencies involved. Each borough has also established a CAMHS core group.

The functions of this group are to:

- work on a multi-agency basis with complex cases;
- offer consultation and liaison on complex cases; and
- feed specific clinical issues to the planning group that need to be considered at a strategic level.

This two-level structure, that links service commissioners with providers and other agencies, is currently being put in place, and has the potential to resolve strategic issues at the health authority level, and to resolve operational issues at the borough/LHG level. While it is not yet fully functioning, it has the potential to link the commissioning activities of the LHGs with the commissioning of Tier 3 and 4 services, and to link more general child and adolescent mental health concerns of the local authority services with the specialist CAMHS through the Gwent Health Improvement Programme.

Assessing needs

84. Health authorities and other agencies should be mapping groups of children and local areas where needs are greatest, and the source of most referrals. Two-thirds of health authorities (64 per cent) reported that they produced large-scale maps showing areas of deprivation. All should do so.

85. Health authorities were found to vary in the extent to which they work closely with other agencies – including trusts – to assess needs [EXHIBIT 29]. Almost half of all trusts (44 per cent) said that they had not been involved by their health authority in any assessment of needs. Most health authorities had involved education and social services authorities in needs assessment, but some key players were less widely involved, including GPs. This will need to change, given that PCGs and LHGs are becoming major players in shaping service provision.

86. Children and their parents should be asked what is important to them and what they think of services. These views may not be easy to obtain, but time and effort should be invested in exploring the views of young people who are, or have been, service-users (Ref. 59). The audits found that only 35 per cent of health authorities had consulted users and carers about services. Where health authorities reported that they had involved users and carers, there were a number of different ways in which this was done. A very few had commissioned specific consultation with young people [CASE STUDY 9]. Others had relied on consultation that had been carried out in developing the local Children's Services Plan or referred to more general user and/or carer consultation carried out by a trust, which had not been geared specifically to the needs for CAMHS. Some reported that what had been learnt from consultation with users and carers had not actually been used to inform service development. All health authorities should be consulting users as part of the planning process.

EXHIBIT 29

Agencies involved in needs assessment and service planning

Some key stakeholders are not widely involved.

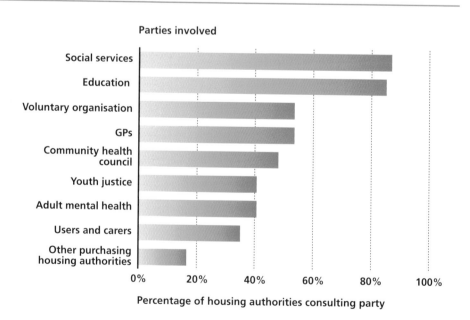

Parties involved

Percentage of housing authorities consulting party

Source: Audit Commission health authority questionnaire database

CASE STUDY 9

Consulting users

Rotherham

In Rotherham, several different methods of gaining the views of young people on mental health services have been tried by a worker whose post is jointly funded by the health authority, trust and local authority. The appointee has:

- developed previous Community Health Council work by talking to a group of schoolchildren;
- conducted a survey of ex-users of CAMHS; and
- conducted a separate questionnaire for children in care.

The results of this work have influenced plans for developing services in Rotherham, including locating more health staff at local social services premises, which are deemed to be more accessible and acceptable to young people.

87. The 1993/94 national review (Ref. 21) reported that population needs assessment had only just begun in some parts of the country. There has been improvement in the five years since, with all health authorities reporting that they are now assessing needs to some extent. While almost all health authorities said that they used at least one standard measure of socio-economic deprivation, such as the Jarman index, they varied in their use of other important sources of information [EXHIBIT 30, overleaf].

EXHIBIT 30

Measures used by health authorities in assessing needs

Health authorities varied in their knowledge and use of important sources of information.

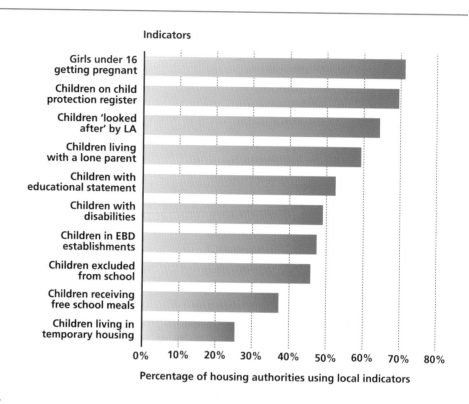

Indicators

Percentage of housing authorities using local indicators

Source: Audit Commission health authority questionnaire database

88. Weaknesses in using local authority information (for example, school exclusions, free school meals, statements of special educational need, and temporary housing) indicate a lack of joint planning, and a potential lack of understanding of local needs for child and adolescent mental health services. Better interagency collaboration is needed to overcome this situation. Many health authorities are aware of the scale of the general task in hand; half considered their assessments to be just 'adequate' or worse [EXHIBIT 31]. Some, however, are adopting a more systematic approach [CASE STUDY 10].

EXHIBIT 31

Health authorities' appraisal of the adequacy of their own needs assessment

Half considered their assessments to be just 'adequate' or worse.

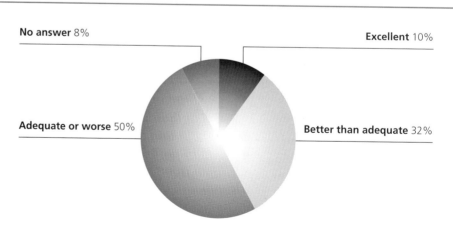

No answer 8%

Excellent 10%

Adequate or worse 50%

Better than adequate 32%

Source: Audit Commission health authority questionnaire database

An example of needs assessment – North and Mid Hants Health Authority

North and Mid Hants Health Authority based its assessment on:

- listing the conditions that it wanted trusts to help with;

- estimating the numbers of children in various parts of the authority who would be expected to present using national prevalence rates;

- adjusting these numbers by known factors that alter vulnerability, such as socio-economic disadvantage; and

- finally adjusting the needs assessment to take into account expected attendance behaviour.

In its report the Health Authority notes:

The population of the ... health authority has a high socio-economic status overall. However, this overall prosperity conceals pockets of deprivation. Twenty-four wards in the health authority (19 per cent) had a deprivation level on the 1991 Census which was equivalent to, or worse than, the average for England and Wales.

and...

Although socio-economic disadvantage can increase the overall amount of disorder, high socio-economic status on the other hand does not make a child immune to psychological and/or psychiatric problems. Some conditions – for example, anorexia, chronic fatigue syndrome and anxiety disorders occur more commonly in those of higher socio-economic status.

An extract of the analysis is shown below for the Health Authority responsible for 136,000 0-18 year olds.

Condition 1: bed wetting

- expected incidence = *8 per cent of 7 year olds falling to 1 per cent of 14 year olds*

- expected in health authority = *2,454*

Condition 2: abdominal pain of unknown cause

- expected incidence = *10 per cent of 5 to 10 year olds*

- expected in health authority = *4,191*

Condition 3: anorexia nervosa

- expected incidence = *0.2 per cent of 11- to 15-year-old girls, 1 per cent of 16- to 18-year-old girls*

- expected in health authority (11 to 15) = *36 x attendance fraction 50 per cent = 18*

- expected in health authority (16 to 18) = *111 x attendance fraction 50 per cent = 56*

Condition 4: attempted suicide

- expected incidence = *2 per cent to 4 per cent of 13 to 18 year olds*

- expected in health authority = *853 to 1,706*

The Health Authority broke down its analysis, which covered 26 separate problems and disorders, into sub-areas of the authority, and then formally reviewed how each of the services provided by a number of different trusts could meet these demands.

Taking stock of resources being used

89. When assessing local needs, agencies must take stock of current services – those provided by the specialist CAMHS, and by other agencies and NHS services. Four out of five health authorities said that they had reviewed, or were reviewing, services. All should undertake such reviews. However, given the generally limited information that services are able to provide regarding their resources and activity, the usefulness of service review is often currently restricted to the task of identifying unmet needs, and the requirements for service development.

90. Where agencies are not working together, gaps or overlaps may occur – either depriving children of the support that they need or wasting scarce skills and resources. Care will be needed to include all the services that are relevant for the mental health of young people. In 1998, the Audit Commission asked social services departments across England and Wales for details of staff who were not part of specialist CAMHS teams but who were working specifically with children and young people with challenging behaviour, or whose emotional development was causing concern. Out of 103 departments that responded, two in five employed such staff – often psychologists – at a total cost of £4 million [TABLE 7].

91. A number of these staff are responsible for providing support and training for residential care workers and foster carers. The largest number provide support and therapy for children and young people who have been abused [EXHIBIT 32]. Several social services departments without such staff reported that they were planning to recruit some, sometimes jointly funding the posts with the health authority.

TABLE 7

Social services staff – not in CAMHS teams

Two in five employed staff – often psychologists.

	County councils	Unitary and met. boroughs	London boroughs	Welsh authorities	Totals
Respondents	25	33	28	17	103
No. with posts	11	14	15	1	41
FTE posts	31	68	28	1	128
Cost (£000s)	827	2,577	550	25	3,979

Source: Audit Commission survey of local authority social services departments, 1998

EXHIBIT 32

Work done by social services
staff not in CAMHS teams

The largest number support those
children who have been abused.

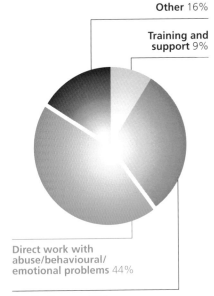

Other 16%

**Training and
support** 9%

**Direct work with
abuse/behavioural/
emotional problems** 44%

Family therapy 31%

*Source: Audit Commission survey of local
authority social services departments*

92. It may be that social services are employing staff with child mental
health expertise as part of their contribution to a carefully constructed
local plan. But it is at least as likely that this is considered necessary
because social services cannot get adequate support from the local
specialist CAMHS. It is important that the mental health input for
children with whom social services are working is planned jointly with
the health authority. Similarly, the needs of education should be assessed
and taken into account.

93. Specialist CAMHS may themselves be fragmented [BOX B]. Although in
many trusts the various professional groups work together in a
co-ordinated way, either in teams or through a more informal network, in
some places their links are tenuous. Psychologists and speech therapists,
in particular, have a wider remit than mental health, and are often core
members of other teams that deal with disability and physical health. This
means that they also operate outside CAMHS. However, having their
own separate caseloads and referral routes puts another obstacle in the
way of co-ordinated child and adolescent mental health services. Children
may be referred simultaneously both to the psychology service and to
CAMHS. Here again, at the very least, the work of these services ought to
be planned to enable complementary and integrated local provision.

BOX B

Fragmented services

One trust has organised its CAMHS
into four quite distinct teams, each
of which operates its own practice.
The result is that the service

provided within the health authority
varies according to where the child
lives. The trust as a whole does not
have a written operational policy

that describes the professional
responsibilities of the staff delivering
CAMHS, and lines of accountability
are therefore also unclear.

	Division 1	Division 2	Division 3	
	Team A	Team B	Team C	Team D
	Full CAMHS mdt[I]	Full CAMHS mdt	Psychiatric services	Psychology services
Social workers involved?	yes	yes	no	no
Waiting times for first assessment?	long	medium	short	unknown
Waiting times for intervention?	reasonable	reasonable	long	unknown

I   mdt: multidisciplinary team.

Transcribing needs into service requirements

94. Once needs have been assessed, current services reviewed and users' views sought, health authorities should work with others to identify the priorities for addressing unmet needs and for developing services. The indicators of needs and the service patterns identified through service review should start to trigger discussions between agencies on key topics:

- Is the right range of services being provided to meet the needs and tackle the risk situations?

- Which services are known to work best for particular problems?

- Are services in the right places?

- Are services being provided in a timely and acceptable manner? Can CAMHS move from being reactive – waiting for problems to get serious before intervening – to being proactive, tackling problems before they get out of hand?

- What role should specialist CAMHS be playing in supporting other agencies in a more skilled and proactive approach?

What works?

95. A major problem in tackling these questions is the gap in knowledge and understanding of 'what works'. There is limited evidence about the efficacy of CAMHS interventions:[1]

It is difficult to demonstrate conclusively a cause and effect relationship between interventions and changes, particularly with children and families who have severe and longstanding difficulties (Ref. 6).

But some findings are beginning to emerge (Ref. 61):

- The most substantial body of research concerns treatments for defined psychiatric conditions in children. There is little research on problems as they present in school or clinic.

- More is known about the treatment of single conditions that are not associated with others, or that do not have serious complicating educational and social problems.

- More is known about the efficacy of treatments with younger children than with adolescents.

- More is known about the shorter- rather than the longer-term effects of treatment.

96. Much still needs to be learnt, but the overall message from research is that many CAMHS interventions are generally associated with significant improvements. Research should be strengthened at every opportunity. A central reference resource (such as Cochrane data bases) would be invaluable to inform staff of up-to-date findings.

---

1   Efficacy is defined as 'the ability of a medical or surgical intervention to produce the desired outcome in a defined population under ideal conditions' (Ref. 60).

Advising and supporting residential social workers may not 'cure' the difficult behaviour of young people in their charge, but may enhance the social workers' ability to deal with it, to the benefit of both themselves and their residents

97. Services that are effective are essentially those that support efficacious interventions and effective clinical work. To date, there is limited but growing evidence on what makes services effective (Ref. 62). But services cannot wait for the outcome of new long-term research before trying to improve their performance. They face a major dilemma. By focusing on what is known to work, they may retreat into providing a relatively narrow range of specialised interventions. In responding to requests for help from education, social services and others, they will broaden their helpful influence but may provide support in ways that are less well proven. Interventions offered for a particular problem may not address the underlying cause but may alleviate many of the resulting difficulties. For instance, a therapeutic approach may not 'cure' a child's developmental disorder, but may improve that child's ability to make friends. And advising and supporting residential social workers may not 'cure' the difficult behaviour of young people in their charge, but may enhance the social workers' ability to deal with it, to the benefit of both themselves and their residents.

98. Assessing the effectiveness of specific interventions and of a child and adolescent mental health service should include many areas and aspects of children's lives and not solely changes in the presenting symptoms (Ref. 63). It is important that CAMHS practitioners contribute to greater knowledge and understanding about the efficacy of interventions and the effectiveness of their services by recording systematically:

- what a holistic appraisal suggests that the child is presenting with;
- what they and others are doing for the child; and
- what the outcomes are.

The effectiveness of services crucially depends not only on offering efficacious treatments with sufficient and appropriately skilled staff to deliver these, but on factors such as access to the service and their acceptability. Recent research (Ref. 64) has begun to show that:

> *The essential ingredient of effectiveness… is not the range of service options, but the human qualities of the individuals who provide these options. If they are not respectful, empathic and genuine, then little they do will be of value to families* (Ref. 65).

Information systems

99. Monitoring outcomes is much helped by appropriate computer support. Local audits found information systems to be particularly variable **(EXHIBITS 27 and 33, overleaf)**. Most trusts tended to generate information on sources of referral, waiting times, numbers referred (and their age and sex) – mainly because commissioners and managers required this information. Fewer had information needed by professionals on the type and severity of problems presented, the types of intervention used, the length of intervention periods, or the numbers of children and young people referred on to other services. Staff in one-quarter (24 per cent) of trusts complained that they spent clinical time in recording information that they never saw again and one-third (36 per cent) of trusts complained that they never received any feedback from information sent to health authorities.

100. Information systems must be developed to support clinical work and to allow audit to be linked to outcomes. Without these, it is not possible to judge what staffing levels and mix may be appropriate to meet the needs of the local child population in achieving good outcomes and good value for money. All who work with children should be recording their presenting problems and outcomes – possibly using tools such as HoNOSCA, or some form of common core data set (Refs. 40 and 66) – so that evidence can gradually be accumulated on what interventions and services work.[1] In time, different services should be able to compare their findings according to standard formats. If this evidence could be collated, perhaps as a result of regional reviews, its usefulness would be further enhanced. Trusts should be strengthening their information systems as a matter of urgency.

I   Further use of HoNOSCA ratings would require their validation and verification and there would be training implications.

EXHIBIT 33

Information routinely available in trusts from computer systems

Trust information systems vary in quality and content – they are particularly poor in relation to the types and severity of the problems seen.

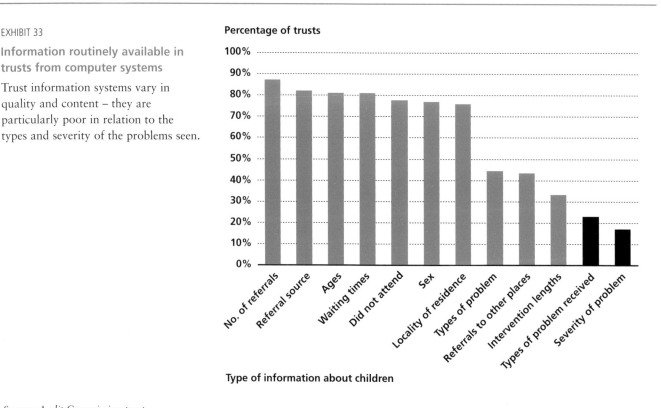

Percentage of trusts

Type of information about children

Source: Audit Commission trust questionnaire database

Specifying requirements

101. The service functions that should be covered in commissioning a comprehensive service for the mental health of children and adolescents were set out by the NHS Health Advisory Service (Ref. 1). Over 90 per cent of health authorities reported that they commissioned, or intended to commission, these functions according to the tiered framework [**EXHIBIT 34**].

102. Just under half of all health authorities had a written policy for securing the mental health of children and young people – with a further one-quarter in the process of developing one.[1] However, only 43 per cent of health authorities had a commissioning plan in place for CAMHS, although a further 55 per cent were working on one. The number of health authorities that had agreed service details with providers varied considerably according to different aspects of the services [**EXHIBIT 35, overleaf**]. In particular, less than one-quarter (23 per cent) of health authorities had specified arrangements for transferring young people to adult services.

---

[1]   This is an increase from 28 per cent in 1993/94 (Ref. 21).

EXHIBIT 34

Functions covered in a comprehensive service for CAMHS

Most were included by more than 80 per cent of health authorities in their commissioning.

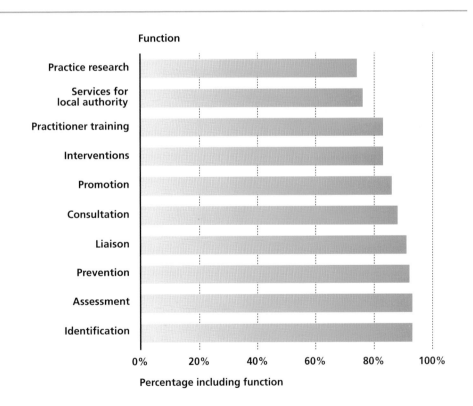

Function

Percentage including function

Source: Audit Commission health authority questionnaire database

Services agreed by health authorities with their providers

Less than one-quarter of health authorities had specified transfer arrangements from CAMHS to adult services.

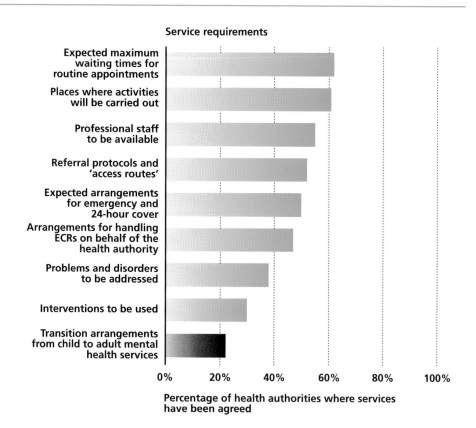

Service requirements

- Expected maximum waiting times for routine appointments
- Places where activities will be carried out
- Professional staff to be available
- Referral protocols and 'access routes'
- Expected arrangements for emergency and 24-hour cover
- Arrangements for handling ECRs on behalf of the health authority
- Problems and disorders to be addressed
- Interventions to be used
- Transition arrangements from child to adult mental health services

0%   20%   40%   60%   80%   100%

Percentage of health authorities where services have been agreed

Source: Audit Commission health authority questionnaire database

103. Health authority service specifications and agreements for specialist CAMHS should start to reflect the changes required to provide a comprehensive service and, in line with the health improvement programme, should influence the purchasing intentions of partner agencies. Where they are doing this, new initiatives can follow [CASE STUDY 11].

Conclusion

104. Progress with commissioning has developed over the five years since it was last surveyed (Ref. 21). Undoubtedly, government guidance and the Health Advisory Service report, *Together We Stand* (Ref. 1), have helped. And the priority given to CAMHS by the current Government is continuing to keep the pressure on. All health authorities should be working with other agencies to assess needs, review services, plan how to set priorities to meet unmet needs, and translate intentions into service agreements that are supported by monitoring systems. All these tasks set a challenging agenda, which is summarised in the next chapter.

CASE STUDY 11

The development of a Community Child and Family Mental Health Service:
South London and Maudsley NHS Trust

Service aims and objectives

The service is a primary and community-based child mental health service working in a socio-economically disadvantaged area of inner London, characterised by high levels of unemployment, poverty and poor housing. It is closely co-ordinated with more specialist child and adolescent mental health teams to form a fully tiered system as envisaged by the Health Advisory Service.

The specific aims of the service are to:

- Improve access to and utilisation of child mental healthcare;
- Improve the identification and management of the broad range of child and family mental health difficulties in the community; and
- Develop community-based health promotion and prevention programmes.

The main emphasis of the service is to enable all community and primary care professionals, such as health visitors, GPs, community paediatricians, school nurses and teachers, to provide skilled child mental healthcare closely supported through training, supervision and consultation by solo child mental health specialists who also undertake direct face-to-face work with troubled children and families in community settings.

Population needs assessment

Prior to the implementation of the clinical projects, the Community Child and Family Service undertook an assessment of local child mental health need and the needs of community and primary care practitioners. The findings confirmed the high prevalence of mental health problems among the local child population and the existence of many child and family vulnerability factors associated with the incidence of such problems.

The clinical projects

1. The Parent Adviser Service
This service involves health visitors and paediatric community doctors, trained by the specialist mental health workers in the skills of parent counselling, parenting and child behaviour management. They work on the basis of home visiting with parents of pre-school children where there are emotional/behavioural problems in the children, psychosocial problems in the parents, or relationship difficulties in the family. Evaluation of the work indicates significant benefits for the families, at least in the short term, in terms of improved maternal self-esteem; reduced maternal stress, depression and anxiety; improvements in the home environment for children, and reduced behavioural and emotional problems in comparison with an untreated waiting list control.

2. Primary Child Mental Health Care Clinics
The Community Child and Family Service has been working with local GP practices since Spring 1996. On-site clinics for children and their families with emotional and behavioural difficulties, conducted by child mental health specialists have been set up in each GP practice. Every opportunity has been taken to establish partnerships with primary healthcare teams rather than to remain as visiting specialists. In addition to direct clinical work, case discussions, joint assessments and clinical advice are also offered to the practice staff, most commonly GPS and health visitors.

By way of evaluation, families complete a set of clinical self-report questionnaires at referral, at four months and at 12 months after their first appointment. Comparison data is being collected from families on the waiting list of a neighbouring child mental health service.

3. School Nurse Training Programme
The model of Parent Adviser work has been extended to school nurses because of the evidence of its effectiveness with children under the age of five. A programme of training and supervision has been run with one group of school nurses.

Continued overleaf

Selected nurses have gone on to identify appropriate children and their families from their current caseload and to work with them as parent advisers. The nurses receive fortnightly group supervision from the project team. Assessments are being made to evaluate the effects of the programme on the nurses and the children with whom they have worked.

4. Intensive School-Based Intervention Programme

In another project, a clinical psychologist has been working for one day a week in a local primary school. The work has provided an opportunity to examine ways in which mental health promotion can occur via a school-based child mental health specialist. The psychologist carries out direct work with pupils and parents referred by the teachers and families themselves; facilitates small problem-focused groups for pupils on issues such as anger control; and provides regular consultation groups for the teaching staff.

There has been enthusiastic support from the school for the direct clinical work. Integration of the aims of the mental health promotion programme with the curriculum has required more

thought. As a result, there has been a shift from whole class work to specific problem-focused groups. The format, membership and content of these have been decided in collaboration with teaching staff and developed in conjunction with a more clearly defined social and personal development curriculum taught on a whole class basis. This programme is now being extended to a number of other schools in the area.

5. Consultation Programme for Day Nursery Officers

An additional means of improving community child mental healthcare and early intervention, particularly for vulnerable children, has been to provide a regular consultation service for day nursery officers. A system has been set up for day nursery staff in the locality to receive fortnightly consultation from a member of the Community Child and Family Service. These sessions are used to discuss children about whom the staff have behavioural, developmental and/or family concerns. They enable the nursery officers to build and test hypotheses about the children; develop a consistent view of their difficulties; examine nursery-parent relations and receive additional

information about child development and mental health. Although the effects are yet to be determined from evaluation, the Community Child and Family Service has already begun to develop an elaborate programme using the Parent Adviser model to train staff from early years centres more extensively and systematically.

6. Primary Prevention of Child Mental Health Problems

A new project has begun which will evaluate the clinical and cost effectiveness of a strategy to promote parents' abilities to care for the psychosocial development of their children and to prevent parental and child problems from arising. Specially trained health visitors conduct promotional interviews before and immediately after all new births, while at the same time screening for families at risk of developing child mental health problems. The health visitors then work immediately and intensively with those identified as being in need. The new service is being evaluated by comparison with the work of health visitors who carry out the same procedures with families, but do not receive the training and supervision of those in the intervention group.

Source: Ref. 67

RECOMMENDATIONS

4 — Working Together

Agencies need to work together and transcribe needs into service requirements. Health authorities should:

1 take the lead in commissioning CAMHS;

2 appoint a member of staff to take the lead as part of a wider multi-agency group for commissioning children's services, which must agree a common approach and be clear about the age range to be covered and about other service boundaries;

3 work with others to identify the priorities for addressing unmet needs and for comprehensive service development, selecting services known to be effective; and

4 ensure that service specifications and agreements for specialist CAMHS start to reflect the changes required to provide a comprehensive service and, in line with the health improvement programme, they should influence the purchasing intentions of partner agencies.

Together, agencies should assess needs and take stock of the resources needed. They should:

5 map groups of children and local areas where needs are greatest, and where most referrals are coming from;

6 consult users and carers;

7 take stock of current services – those provided by the specialist CAMHS, by other agencies and by other NHS services; and

8 develop information systems that support clinical work and allow audit and service evaluation linked to agreed outcomes.

5

Moving Forward

The progress overall of health authorities and trusts in
commissioning and providing CAMHS was found to be
variable, with some well advanced, but others less so.
Authorities and trusts which are not addressing good practice
issues satisfactorily will find themselves increasingly adrift of
the rapidly developing agenda. To support and co-ordinate
improvements, action is needed at both national and local
levels. This report proposes action, building on
recommendations in previous chapters, to provide a
comprehensive agenda for the future.

Overall progress

105. The previous two chapters have reviewed progress over a wide range of issues. Some authorities and trusts are making good progress and others are making more limited advances. To assess overall progress, a set of quality indicators was developed from factors explored through the questionnaires used in the local audits. These indicators were based on authoritative published work. They were discussed in depth with the steering group for the national Audit Commission project, and subsequently refined (Appendix 3).

106. Health authorities and trusts were scored in relation to each indicator and the scores added across all indicators. Reflecting their overall progress, certain health authorities and trusts were identified with high scores and others with low scores. Further information to help to understand the reasons why certain health authorities and trusts were scored as doing well, and others as doing poorly, was sought through in-depth discussion with a group of auditors who had worked closely with both high- and low-scoring authorities and trusts. Further information was also obtained from a number of auditors' detailed reports. The following key issues were identified.

Health authorities

107. Low-scoring health authorities usually had a multidisciplinary group with a designated lead person for developing a strategy for CAMHS, but if the lead person had insufficient authority, commissioning was likely to be ineffective. Low-scoring authorities lacked adequate population needs assessment and made little use of information routinely collected by the local authority. They also lacked adequate reviews of services, and often excluded non-NHS services. Although they might have purchasing agreements with social services and education, there was no evidence of joint interagency strategic development. GPs were often not involved in the development of any strategy – which is particularly critical, given the introduction of primary care groups and local health groups. None of the low scorers had involved neighbouring health authorities in joint commissioning for Tier 4 services. Arrangements for emergency and 24-hour cover, and for handling ECRs, were not in place, nor were maximum waiting times or referral access routes agreed.

108. In contrast, health authorities with evidence of good commissioning had paid specific attention to the interfaces between the four tiers of services, ensuring ready access to appropriate levels and types of expertise, with continuing support after 'discharge' from any particular service.

What distinguished the high-scoring trusts, above all, seemed to be clear, informed, imaginative and understanding management of the service

109. No relationship was found between the amount spent per head by a health authority on CAMHS and other indications of the quality of their commissioning [EXHIBIT 36].

Trusts

110. The over-riding characteristic of the low-scoring trusts was the lack of a designated manager or lead clinician to head the specialist CAMHS. Priorities for the service were not clear, with no strategic direction and no service specification, let alone one that had been agreed with the health authority or tailored to meet assessed needs. The amount and quality of information about the specialist CAMHS were almost universally poor, and, as a result, the capacity to monitor activity (even DNA rates) and outcomes was almost non-existent.

111. CAMHS in low-scoring trusts lacked specialists who should have been a key part of a multidisciplinary team – notably clinical psychologists, child psychotherapists and social workers. Low-scoring trusts reported having no special interests in particular services, such as for eating disorders or work with adolescents. Waiting times after referral acceptance were long. Usually referrals were limited to those from GPs. Contact with local social services, education, and youth justice services was limited to infrequent advice on specific cases. Many of these services also placed limits on the age range of children seen, usually up to 16 years but sometimes only up to age 14. Child and adolescent psychiatrists spent perhaps 70 per cent of their time on face-to-face work with individual children and spent little or no time on liaison, consultation, supervision and training with others. Unqualified clinical psychiatrists were employed in some instances. These trusts were unlikely to have training funds allocated for CAMHS.

112. What distinguished the high-scoring trusts, above all, seemed to be clear, informed, imaginative and understanding management of the service. Interestingly, in view of earlier observations, many small trusts had high scores, and the overall indicator of quality was not associated with trust size [EXHIBIT 37]. In these trusts, purposeful leadership and management appeared to be important in overcoming any disadvantages of being small.

EXHIBIT 36

Health authority quality indicator score compared with spend per head

No relationship was found.

Quality Indicator Score

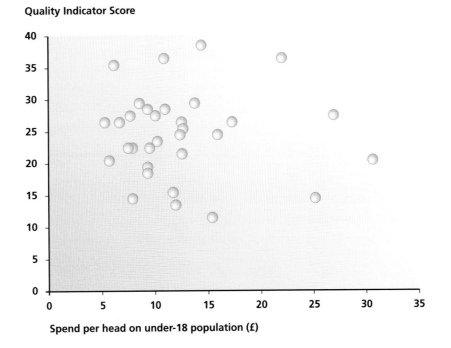

Spend per head on under-18 population (£)

Source: Audit Commission analysis

EXHIBIT 37

Trust quality indicator score compared with size (full-time equivalent staff numbers)

Many small trusts had high scores on quality indicators.

Quality Indicator Score

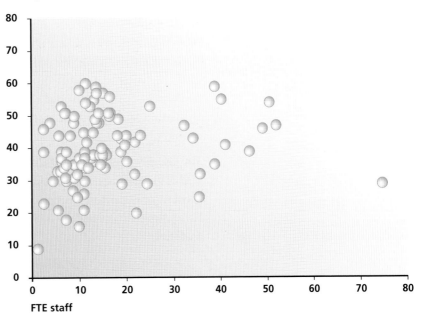

FTE staff

Source: Audit Commission analysis

Next steps

Central reference systems that inform the field of up-to-date ideas, and information about good practice in commissioning and service provision, should be supported

113. The audits of health authorities and trusts that were carried out during 1998/99 have revealed progress in the commissioning of services for the mental health of children and adolescents in England and Wales, and in the provision of specialist CAMHS.[I] However, to effect improvement in the mental health of young people, further development is required. Authorities and trusts who are not addressing the issues discussed in this report satisfactorily will find themselves increasingly adrift, given the rapidly developing agenda. To help to direct the actions needed, the following proposals are made, first at the national level and second at the local level. These build on, and extend, the recommendations made in previous chapters to provide a comprehensive agenda for the future.

Nationally

114. Central reference systems that inform the field of up-to-date ideas, and information about good practice in commissioning and service provision, should be supported. The key is to bring together the elements needed to develop a comprehensive framework for CAMHS, in line with the national service framework for mental health (Modernising Mental Health Services), which focuses on mental illness in adults. Such a framework should inform local health improvement programmes and, through these, local commissioning.[II]

115. Use of the Common Core Data Set (such as that developed for the Association of Child Psychologists, and Psychiatrists) (Ref. 66) should be promoted, and further developed for recording the types of problems in children who present to services. Similarly, using a standard set of outcome measures (such as the Health of the Nation Outcome Scales for Children and Adolescents – HoNOSCA) (Ref. 40) should be promoted to evaluate both the work of the specialist CAMHS and wider services for child and adolescent mental health. To support 'joined-up' service evaluation and development, outcomes should be sought for all aspects of a child's life, and across the whole system of care (Ref. 62).

116. The development of information systems that are suitable for CAMHS should be supported, in line with those for other services, taking account of opportunities presented by the national information strategy. Investment in appropriate compatible computerised systems will be essential.

I   Along the lines suggested in guidance published up to 1995 and measured against the findings of the 1993/94 national survey (Ref. 21).

II   The framework would bring together research and continuing service evaluation evidence (for example, from CAMHS Innovation Mental Health Grant projects) from many sources and make these easily available. The work of HAS 2000 and of Young Minds needs to be reviewed along with other initiatives, such as the NHS R&D funded systematic review of the effectiveness of interventions in child and adolescent mental health, carried out by Professor Peter Fonagy and colleagues at University College, London (Ref. 37).

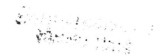

An over-arching review of the impact of different national policy initiatives should be maintained, so that different initiatives reinforce each other

117. Joint health and local authority reviews of services for the mental health of children and adolescents should be supported, and development work facilitated for authorities and agencies that need it. Particular attention should be paid to the adequacy of resources allocated to this increasingly important field, and to supporting changes over the long term.

118. Professional organisations and others, as appropriate, should support training in specific treatments (for example, the management of postnatal depression by health visitors), and in new ways of working that have shown promise (for example, primary mental healthcare services).

119. An over-arching review of the impact of different national policy initiatives should be maintained, so that different initiatives reinforce each other. Many major national initiatives, such as health action zones, education action zones, the Quality Protects programme, Sure Start and the Crime Prevention Strategy have the potential to make improvements in child and adolescent mental health in many parts of England and Wales. Ways should be found to support and develop local statutory and voluntary sector services as a result of these initiatives.

There is a need to ensure that any move of commissioning of CAMHS from health authorities to PCGs does not lose such expertise as is available

Local commissioning

120. Health and local authorities should work with others, including the voluntary sector, to develop the commissioning of Tier 1 services for promoting children's mental health, preventing problems, and early identification and intervention, building a co-ordinated network of local provision across services and agencies.

121. They should specify ways to co-ordinate the implementation of policies in education (notably behaviour support planning), social services (under the 'Quality Protects' programme), and youth justice (notably, youth offending teams), so that the efforts in all sectors are neither wasted nor unsupported, but are reinforced by each other. This requires commissioning for child and adolescent mental health services and children's services planning to be closely integrated. There is a need to ensure that any move of commissioning of CAMHS from health authorities to PCGs does not lose such expertise as is available, and that health authorities together with local authorities remain closely involved in offering advice on strategic planning.

122. They should commission and specify jointly with other local agencies (and with other health authorities, as appropriate) suitable provision for groups of young people requiring intensive assessment and treatment, and particular types of approach and facilities (for example, children looked after by the local authority, children excluded from school, children of mentally ill parents, children with learning disability, and children in the youth justice system). There is scope for deciding on the value to be gained by pooling budgets for specific services under the 'Partnership in Action' agenda.

123. **Health authorities** should ensure that guidance under the National Service Framework for mental illness is followed where it applies to services for children and adolescents. Adult and children's mental health services should work more closely together to support children of mentally ill parents, and to provide sensitive and appropriate arrangements for adolescents in transition to adult services.

124. They should include child and adolescent mental health in their health improvement programme and in line with local authority children's services planning, should work with primary care groups to develop multi-agency local commissioning of CAMHS.

125. They should ensure comprehensive and equitable provision of services for the mental health of children and adolescents in their population, paying particular attention to the availability of appropriate resources and skills for 24-hour cover and emergency responses.

126. They should set up mechanisms for obtaining the views, systematically and regularly, of users and carers on how services can best meet their needs, and for incorporating these into their service planning and monitoring activities. There should also be up-to-date information about the services for users and carers, and regular feedback to them.

127. They should specify ways in which Tier 2 and 3 services can:

- develop their role in training and supporting Tier 1 services;
- develop specialist expertise in particular areas of work, such as that with adolescents;
- work more closely with Tier 4, particularly in the follow-up and continuing care of young people leaving Tier 4 services; and
- become more expert in understanding the work with complex cases.

128. They should commission and specify appropriate information systems and procedures whereby information will be used to inform future commissioning. In particular, they should consider how the outcomes of service provision will be monitored.

129. They should link service specification to financial planning and purchasing in order to ensure value for money.

130. Providers of specialist CAMHS together with commissioners should agree the boundaries of, and a specification for, the service that they will provide, in terms of the characteristics and problems of the young people to be served and the assessment and treatment approaches to be offered. A budget should be negotiated that covers delivery of the agreed service.

131. They should designate a manager with sufficient experience to lead, and to take responsibility and be accountable for, the specialist CAMHS. There must also be clear and agreed lines of clinical responsibility for all professional staff.

132. They should review the numbers and type of staff whom they employ and the skills they bring to bear, and make sure that they have sufficient numbers of staff with the right skills to meet commissioners' specifications. It is important that the different elements of the specialist service are clinically and managerially co-ordinated so that they meet children's needs as effectively and efficiently as possible.

133. They should inform themselves of the up-to-date evidence regarding the efficacy of interventions in child and adolescent mental health and good practice in service delivery, and make plans to develop their service accordingly. This approach is likely to require some reconfiguration of the service, and staff training.

134. They should negotiate on the amount and form of support needed for Tier 1 services, and ensure that they are able to provide this.

135. They should consider how to promote greater integration with the services of other agencies and adult mental health services, particularly in addressing the needs of young people known to be at high risk of mental problems, such as children looked after by the local authority and the children of mentally ill parents. Integrated services from a number of agencies must also be planned for the continuing support of some young people over long periods.

136. They should develop and agree quality standards for their services – particularly with regard to waiting times and DNA rates – and review problem areas such as accommodation. Adherence to standards should be monitored regularly. It is important that the views of children, adolescents and families are obtained and used to inform all aspects of the quality of service provision.

137. They should improve information systems, not just to provide better management information, but to support ongoing clinical audit and service evaluation. This will mean standardising the way that sources of referral, problems presenting, interventions used and outcomes achieved are recorded.

Conclusion

138. This is an ambitious and challenging agenda. In England the extra resources being made available will help authorities and trusts to start to tackle this agenda. In Wales, the establishment of the Advisory Group and the All-Wales Strategy for CAMHS will help to take the agenda forward. But though challenging, the achievement of this agenda should improve the lives of many children and young people who are among some of the most disadvantaged in our society.

Appendix 1

Members of the advisory group

Professor Peter Hill	Professor of Child and Adolescent Psychiatry Great Ormond Street Hospital for Sick Children
Dr Richard Ayres	Consultant Child Psychiatrist Swindon & Marlborough NHS Trust
Barry Webb	Assistant Director of Health Strategy Wiltshire HA
Eva Holmes	Retired Director of Enfield Child and Family Services
Dr Bob Jezzard	NHS Executive
Peter Wilson	Director, Young Minds
Professor Hilton Davis	Professor of Child Health Psychology South London and Maudsley NHS Trust
Hilary Rowland	Audit Commission Member, and Chief Executive of Royal Liverpool Children's NHS Trust

Appendix 2

The prevalence of mental health problems in young people

The number of children in any community that suffer from mental health problems is considerable. The earliest studies in England – carried out in the 1960s by Rutter and colleagues in the Isle of Wight – showed a prevalence of 12 per cent among 9- to 11-year-old children (Refs. 68 and 69).

Variation in prevalence rates began to be reported shortly after, with consistently higher rates found in urban compared with more rural areas (Ref. 69). As evidence from rigorous studies from many parts of the world accumulated, it became clear that the prevalence of childhood mental health disorder also varied according to:

- the methods of assessment used in studies;
- the definition used of what constitutes a case of disorder; and
- the age group studied, as well as other characteristics of the study sample (Ref. 70).

A diagnosis of psychiatric disorder, according to the established medical diagnostic categories, can be made in between 10 per cent and 33 per cent of the child population at any one time, with a fairly close consensus on a prevalence rate of 20 per cent (Ref. 2). The rates tend to be lower if the case definition depends upon a certain threshold of severity and/or impairment of function, and are higher in older children, and in those with certain characteristics and living in certain circumstances (Ref. 37).

The prevalence of particular disorders also varies according to age and, to some extent, sex, but overall:

- anxiety disorders affect around 12 per cent of children;
- disruptive disorders (which are chiefly classified as conduct disorders), around 10 per cent;
- attention deficit hyperactivity disorder (ADHD), perhaps 5 per cent; and
- depression, specific developmental disorders, enuresis, and substance abuse, up to 6 per cent, depending on age group.

Pervasive developmental disorders such as autistic disorders, and psychoses are rare, affecting fewer than 1 per cent of young people under the age of 18 years (Ref. 2). Many children present with more than one disorder (Refs. 45 and 46).

The extent and type of mental health problems vary in children according to certain predisposing characteristics such as brain damage and physical or learning disability. Certain family situations and circumstances with which they grow up may also increase the risk of children sustaining mental health problems. These 'risk factors' are given below:

Factors that increase the risk of mental health problems in young people:

1. **Child risk factors**

- Genetic influences
- Low IQ and learning disability
- Specific developmental delay
- Communication difficulty
- Difficult temperament
- Physical illness, especially if chronic and/or neurological
- Academic failure
- Low self-esteem

2. **Family risk factors**

- Overt parental conflict
- Family breakdown
- Inconsistent or unclear discipline
- Hostile and rejecting relationships
- Failure to adapt to the child's changing developmental needs
- Abuse – physical, sexual and/or emotional
- Parental psychiatric illness
- Parental criminality, alcoholism, and personality disorder
- Death and loss – including loss of friendships

3. **Environmental risk factors**

- Socio-economic disadvantage
- Homelessness
- Disaster
- Discrimination
- Other significant life events

In recent times, attention has also been directed to understanding why it is that many children who suffer adverse circumstances and a combination of risk factors do not develop mental health problems. Three key groups of factors appear to protect young people:

- Self-esteem, sociability, and autonomy;
- Family compassion, warmth, and absence of parental discord; and
- Social support systems that encourage personal effort and coping.

Source: Ref. 71

Appendix 3

Quality checklists

Drawing upon the sources referred to in the first chapter, the Audit Commission identified that good practice in commissioning and providing CAMHS should be based on:

- evidence from the scientific literature about what works;
- equitable access;
- service acceptability to enable optimal compliance with treatment and management;
- maintenance of staff skills and morale;
- planned and agreed prioritisation of cases;
- management of the whole child and of relevant contextual factors;
- maximum participation of the child or young person in decisions with full consideration given to their wishes; and
- optimal use of expensive resources.

These features are developed in Box C.

BOX C

Good quality in commissioning, purchasing and providing

The health authority will generally be the lead agency in commissioning services for the mental health of children and adolescents.

Health commissioners should work with their providers, local authorities and with other agencies to:

- recognise the importance of child and adolescent mental health;
- commission services for the mental health of children and adolescents in close collaboration with each other. The involvement of users and carers is important;
- assess the mental health needs of their child and adolescent populations;
- review services provided by all relevant agencies comprehensively, to include the level and type of available resources, their effectiveness, access, acceptability and other aspects of service quality;
- identify unmet needs and decide on priorities for service development;
- ensure that a range of services is flexibly provided through service agreements and contracts as appropriate. This provision should cover:
  - promotion of mental health;
  - prevention of problems and disorders;
  - identification and assessment of problems and disorders;

BOX C (continued)

- – intervention and management approaches;
- – liaison and consultation work with other NHS and non-NHS agencies;
- – practitioner supervision and training; and
- – practice research and service evaluation;
- ensure the availability of an appropriate range of clearly specified specialist services, and agree access routes;
- ensure the availability of 24-hour and emergency cover for young people presenting with mental health problems; and
- develop the capability of local information systems to support needs assessment, resource management, joint planning and purchasing across agencies, monitoring care delivery, measuring effectiveness, and to support clinical and management audit.

Providers should agree with their commissioners:

- A **service specification** with clear aims and objectives for:
  - – the needs its services aim to meet; and
  - – the ways in which needs will be met, including the interventions to be provided.
- A **budget**, designated separately for CAMHS, which should include an agreed level of funding for direct referrals from, and for informal work with, education and social services, as well as a demonstrable commitment to provide adequate specialist mental health support to social workers, teachers, the courts and others working with young people; and
- **Staffing** sufficient to offer a range of interventions, and an appropriate mix and balance of expertise. Specialist services operating at Tiers 2, 3 and 4 should normally include a mix of staff across a number of disciplines that might include child and adolescent psychiatry, clinical and educational psychology, child mental health nursing, child psychotherapy and social work.

Although there is no single recipe for the way in which disciplines work well together, nor for the appropriate mix and size of a team, there is a size of team below which both the capability and the viability of the service is called into question. Providers should recognise staff training needs and devise ways of meeting them.

There should be a balance between direct work with children and families, and indirect work such as providing consultation and training for other professionals and agencies. Unidisciplinary work and multidisciplinary teamwork should both be available to cover the spectrum of needs, and professional isolation should be avoided.

BOX C (continued)

- **Operational arrangements**, including:
  - a designated manager for the service; and
  - effective co-ordination of the services, with clear protocols for working with other agencies to provide the multi-faceted interventions known to be the most effective for many child and adolescent mental health problems. The service, and the individual professionals within it, need to have clearly defined roles and responsibilities, with systems for professional and managerial accountability.
- **Quality standards** with performance and outcome measures which include:
  - accessibility – for example, waiting times and referral criteria;
  - acceptability – for example, child-friendly environments, and sessions held at a variety of settings;
  - support to non-specialist staff – for example, assistance and advice to teachers or GPs;
  - staff skills and activity – for example, nurses trained to work both with children and in mental health;
  - DNA ('did not attend') rates that are monitored and the reasons addressed;
  - use of effective treatment approaches; and
  - outcomes – assessed in a number of domains – for example, in symptoms, function and client satisfaction.
- **An information system** capable of monitoring these standards is essential. It should also support resource management and clinical audit.

Source: Audit Commission based on the outcome of previous research in CAMHS (Refs. 1, 6, 17, 21, 38)

To illustrate progress in these areas, the Audit Commission produced a checklist based on questions asked in the audit questionnaires at the health authorities and NHS trusts. Each of an early sample of trusts and health authorities[1] was scored on its overall achievement in answering the questions.

---

[1] 44 health authorities and 106 trusts.

Quality indicators for commissioners and purchasers of CAMHS

Process

1. There is a member of staff acting as health authority lead officer for services for child and adolescent mental health.

2. This lead officer is part of an interagency group and the group membership comprises at least nine of the following: child and adolescent psychiatry, psychology, adult mental health, child health/paediatrics, non-clinical managers, general practitioners, local social services, local education services, local youth justice/probation services, community health council, voluntary organisations, users and carers, and others.

3. A comprehensive service includes all ten of the following functions: promotion of mental health, prevention of problems and disorders, identification of problems and disorders, assessment, treatment and management approaches, liaison and consultation, statutory duties (such as court reports), practice and service evaluation and research, practitioner training and supervision.

4. The HA has a written policy.

Needs assessment

5. The HA uses at least fifteen of the following measures: adult population, child population (aged 0 to 17 years), child sub-populations (ages 0 to 4, 5 to 11, 12 to 15, 16 to 17), birth rate, perinatal mortality rate, under 16 pregnancy rate, proportion of lone parent families, number of children in temporary housing, number receiving free school meals, number on the child protection register, number of children on disability registers, number of children with statements of special educational needs, number of school exclusions, number in EBD education establishments, number of children 'looked after' by the LA.

6. The HA uses a standard indicator (Jarman or Townsend or similar) to map areas of socio-economic deprivation.

7. Users and carers have been involved in the assessment of needs.

8. The HA has involved at least nine of those listed (in 2) in carrying out an assessment of needs.

9. The HA considers its needs assessment to be excellent or better than adequate.

Service review

10. The HA has reviewed the availability of all services for child and adolescent mental health.

11. The HA funds agencies with a specific remit to promote children's mental health.

12. The HA funds agencies with a specific remit to prevent the development of mental health problems and disorders.

Commissioning

13. The HA has a written policy for securing the mental health of its children and young people.

14. The HA has a commissioning plan or is working on one.

15. The commissioning strategy covers all four tiers.

16. The commissioning strategy covers interfaces between the tiers.

The strategy is linked to:

17. commissioning for child health

18. commissioning for adult mental health services

19. LA Children's Services planning.

20. The HA has a development plan designed to address each of its limitations and service quality issues.

21. The CAMHS commissioning strategy is linked to HA financial planning.

Service specification

There is a service specification covering:

22. Tier 2

23. Tier 3

24. Tier 4 inpatient services.

There are specifications for:

25. adolescents

26. children looked after by the LA

27. children with learning difficulties.

The HA has agreed with providers:

28. expected arrangements for emergency and 24-hour cover

29. arrangements for handling ECRs

30. maximum waiting times for routine appointments

31. transition arrangements from child to adult mental health services

32. referral access routes.

Collaborative arrangements are specified with:

33. Social services

34. Education

35. Youth justice.

Budgets and contracts

36. The HA spends some money on LA services.

37. The HA spends less than 25 per cent on ECRs.

38. The HA has made joint arrangements with other HAs.

The HA has made joint purchasing agreements with:

39. Education.

40. Social services.

41. The HA receives satisfactory information for monitoring purposes.

42. The HA has commissioned research and/or evaluation in CAMHS.

FINDINGS

The maximum possible score was 42.

11 out of 44 HAs scored between 28 and 38.

13 scored 20 or below.

Highest = 38

Lowest = 6

Quality indicators for providers of CAMHS

Background

1. The trust holds regular sessions at three or more of the following locations: hospital or hospital site, community-based clinic, GP surgery or primary healthcare setting, social services setting, education establishment, other.

The trust makes assessments and/or carries out treatments at the child's:

2. family home

3. other residential accommodation

4. school.

5. The trust has special CAMHS teams or projects and services that it considers to be innovative.

Service specification

6. The trust has a detailed specification for the specialist CAMHS.

7. The trust contributed to the HA assessment of population needs for CAMHS.

8. The trust contributed to a HA service review for CAMHS.

Information capability

The trust can access data on:

9. six or more of the following referral details: sources of referral, number of children referred, ages, sex, locality of residence, types of problem, trends in any of the above

10. waiting times

11. length of treatment episodes

12. DNA rates by clinic

13. Number of children referred on annually

14. Types of problem referred on.

Operations – planning and practice

The trust has an operational plan that defines:

15. age ranges

16. groups at risk

17. types of problem or disorder

18. geographical location.

The trust offers the following functions:

19. promotion of mental health

20. prevention of problems and disorders

21. assessment

22. intervention and management approaches

23. services for local authorities

24. practice research and evaluation

25. practitioner training

26. liaison with other NHS and non-NHS services

27. consultation with other NHS services

28. consultation with non-NHS services.

The trust has set its sources of referral and these include:

29. GPs

30. paediatricians

31. clinical psychologists

32. child health nurses

33. drug and alcohol services

34. learning disability services

35. Education

36. Social services

37. relevant local voluntary organisations

38. self-referral.

Criteria for onward referral have been:

39. set by trust

40. agreed with the commissioners

41. agreed with the agencies to whom referred.

42. Median waiting time for a non-emergency is twelve weeks or less.

43. The waiting time is conditional on assessment of priority.

The trust:

44. monitors DNA rates

45. its average DNA rate is less than 18 per cent of all those referred

46. There are routine procedures for follow-up of young people who do not keep appointments.

47. The trust considers it has access to appropriately skilled 24-hour cover.

48. The trust considers it has adequate systems to respond effectively to young people presenting in crisis.

49. The trust has a written operational policy on the roles, professional relationships and responsibilities of the different professionals involved in the CAMHS.

50. The organisation of the CAMHS staff into teams or otherwise is clearly set out.

51. The arrangements for clinical supervision are clear and agreed.

Finance and budgets

52. The trust can show the various sources of income for the CAMHS.

The trust has used specific funds for:

53. clinical audit

54. training

55. research or evaluation.

Adequacy of professional resources

56. The CAMHS team members include at least three different professions.

The trust has information:

57. on CAMHS staff activity **and** it covers all teams and localities

58. which distinguishes between direct and indirect casework.

59. There is a training budget **and** it is over 5 per cent of the total CAMHS income.

Good practice

The trust considers it has developed a policy of good practice in at least five of the following six areas:

60. access for particular groups of children

61. child-centred approaches to service provision

62. child protection

63. age-appropriate facilities and approaches

64. confidentiality

65. complaints.

The trust has a programme within CAMHS of:

66. clinical audit

67. financial/management audit

68. evidence-based service evaluation.

69. There is joint service evaluation with other agencies.

70. The trust has a development plan for CAMHS.

FINDINGS

The maximum possible score was 70.

20 out of 106 trusts scored between 50 and 67.

20 scored 30 or below.

Highest = 67

Lowest = 8

Appendix 4

Audit objectives, methodology and sites

This appendix summarises key points about the national audits carried out in 1998 and 1999. The appendix contains edited material from a national CAMHS audit guide – published in January 1998 – and from other audit documentation developed in the first half of 1998.

Reasons for the audit – why review CAMHS?

Four reasons were identified:

1st reason
CAMHS was high on the national agenda. There was concern over the patchiness of services, and all HAs were required to produce a strategy for the mental health of children and adolescents.

2nd reason
The costs of CAMHS were largely unknown – or at best known only approximately because of the range of contributions from a wide variety of providing authorities.

3rd reason
In trusts CAMHS had often been a Cinderella-service – squeezed by more influential specialties. CAMHS was also known to be fragmented; professionals had become isolated and lacked reliable comparative information on recognised good practice both in terms of responding to commissioners and in organising the trust's internal CAMHS operation.

4th reason
CAMHS had been alluded to on several occasions in previous nationally-delivered Audit Commission audits – but had never been the subject of a single dedicated audit.

The audit was designed to cover both health authorities and NHS trusts. The Audit Commission expected:

- a short audit to be carried out in all HAs; and
- a wider audit to be carried out in all trusts delivering CAMHS.

Exploratory work and pilot audits had been carried out in 11 HAs and 15 trusts. The responses had been positive, and had led to a better understanding of:

- the commissioning process in general;
- the use of professional time;
- service demand patterns; and
- service gaps and weaknesses.

As a result the audit was given the full backing of the Department of Health and various organisations representing CAMHS professionals.

Scope, key issues and objectives of the audit

The focus of the CAMHS audit was strategic, concerned with matters like:

- policy setting;
- interagency agreements;
- contract specification; and
- service delivery against contracts.

It was to focus on specialist CAMHS (tiers 2, 3 and 4), and would **not** look in detail at the roles of health visitors, health promotion or GPs beyond what was covered in the HA audit in considering '*service comprehensiveness*'. The audit asked questions on:

- how commissioners decided what services they needed;
- how professionals spent their time;
- how referrals were processed; and
- how contracts were monitored.

In most instances these 'how' questions were asked to judge something more strategic rather than to provide a conduit to operational matters. For example, although the audit asked questions which sought to find out whether there was joint commissioning and whether there was multi-disciplinary team working, the auditor was not expected to pursue these issues further in the audit.

The HA and trust audits each had a key objective. This key objective was informed, in each case, by six prime indicators.

HA audit
Objective
To identify the extent to which the authority commissions and purchases, with others, a comprehensive service for the mental health of children and adolescents.

Prime indicators
1. The HA has agreed, with other agencies, a definition of comprehensive services for the mental health of children and adolescents.
2. The HA has the necessary information for assessing needs, and has worked through a proper assessment process.
3. The HA has conducted a review of services available for young people's mental health including those provided by agencies outside the NHS; service strengths, shortfalls and development priorities have been established.
4. The HA has a strategy for commissioning and purchasing the specialist child and adolescent mental health services (CAMHS).
5. Service specifications have been prepared in line with the plan for specialist CAMHS.
6. CAMHS contracts are in place in line with service specifications, and contract monitoring is appropriate.

Trust audit

Objective

To identify the extent to which the NHS trust provides a range of specialist child and adolescent mental health services (CAMHS) in accordance with its contracts, and the recommendations set out in national reports.

Prime indicators

1. The trust has agreed CAMH service specification with its purchasers

2. The trust has agreed an operational plan to guide the delivery of its specialist CAMH service

3. The trust knows the sources of its CAMHS income, and the destinations of its CAMHS expenditure

4. The trust has sufficient professional expertise to deliver the range and type of service agreed with purchasers

5. The trust works with primary care and other health services, as well as other agencies, and has developed contractual and other formal joint working arrangements with them

6. The trust addresses good practice issues.

The audit used five data-gathering instruments:

*   two questionnaires, one for commissioners and one for providers, which revealed through interviews the overall shape of the services purchased and provided;

*   two caseload survey forms for CAMHS professionals. These gathered information on the children presenting for assessment and treatment over a four-week period; and

*   a diary form for the same CAMHS professionals. Again, this ran for four weeks and collected information on how professionals used their time.

Data processing

It was known that the CAMHS audit would generate considerable new data. A disk containing re-formattable versions of the two questionnaires was included with the audit guide. Auditors were expected to key in their answers, but not to edit or delete questions or to change the order of the questions. Auditors sent copies of the completed forms to the Audit Commission. Various information was extracted from the form and keyed on to a national data base. This was subsequently analysed and returned to local auditors so that they could compare their own HA and/or trust with other HAs/trusts.

The Audit Commission negotiated a separate contract with a commercial bureau to scan the data from the diary and caseload exercises. Scanned data was written to an Access database which was later converted to Excel spreadsheet format for local audit use.

Appendix 5

The HoNOSCA methodology

Health of the Nation Outcome Scales for Children and Adolescents (HoNOSCA)

HoNOSCA was designed primarily as an outcome measure to measure progress in the care of patients (Ref.40). The following are the categories and problems included in the scales:

1. **Problems with disruptive, antisocial or aggressive behaviour**
   - Includes behaviour associated with any disorder, such as hyperkinetic disorder, depression, autism, drugs or alcohol.
   - Includes physical or verbal aggression (e.g. pushing, hitting, vandalism, teasing), or physical or sexual abuse of other children.
   - Includes antisocial behaviour (e.g. thieving, lying, cheating) or oppositional behaviour (e.g. defiance, opposition to authority or tantrums).
   - Does not include overactivity (rated at scale 2), truancy (rated at scale 13), or self-harm (rated at scale 3).

2. **Problems with overactivity, or attention or concentration**
   - Includes overactive behaviour associated with any cause such as hyperkinetic disorder, mania or arising from drugs.
   - Includes problems with overactive behaviour, restlessness or fidgeting or inattention, or concentration due to any cause.

3. **Non-accidental self-injury**
   - Includes self-harm such as hitting self and self-cutting. Suicide attempts: overdoses, hanging, drowning etc.
   - Does not include scratching, or other accidental self-injury due to physical illness or severe learning or physical disability (rated at scale 6), or illness or injury as a direct consequence of drug/alcohol use (rated at scale 4).

4. **Problems with alcohol, substance/solvent misuse**
   - Includes problems with alcohol substance/solvent misuse taking into account current age and societal norms.
   - Does not include aggressive/disruptive behaviour due to alcohol or drug use (rated at scale 1). Physical illness or disability due to alcohol or drug use (rated at scale 6).

5. **Problems with scholastic or language skills**
   - Includes problems in reading, spelling, arithmetic, speech, or language associated with any disorder or problem, such as a specific developmental learning problem, or physical disability such as a hearing problem.
   - Includes reduced scholastic performance associated with emotional or behavioural problems.

- Does not include children with generalised learning disability unless their functioning is below the expected level.
- Does not include temporary problems resulting purely from inadequate education.

6. **Physical illness or disability problems**

- Includes physical illness or disability problems that limit or prevent movement, impair sight or hearing, or otherwise interfere with personal functioning.
- Includes movement disorder, side effects from medication, physical effects from drug/alcohol use, or physical complications of psychological disorders such as severe weight loss.
- Includes consequences of self-injury such as head banging, arising from learning or physical disability.
- Does not include somatic complaints with no organic basis (rated at scale 8).

7. **Problems associated with hallucinations, delusions, abnormal perceptions or beliefs**

- Includes hallucinations and delusions or abnormal perceptions irrespective of diagnosis.
- Includes odd and bizarre behaviour associated with hallucinations and delusions.
- Includes problems with other abnormal perceptions such as illusions or pseudo-hallucinations, or over-valued ideas such as distorted body image, suspicious or paranoid thoughts.
- Does not include disruptive or aggressive behaviour associated with hallucinations or delusions (rated at scale 2).

8. **Problems with non-organic somatic symptoms**

- Includes problems with gastrointestinal symptoms such as non-organic vomiting or cardiovascular symptoms or neurological symptoms, or non-organic enuresis or encopresis or sleep problems or chronic fatigue.
- Does not include movement disorders such as tics (rated at scale 6); or physical illnesses that complicate non-organic somatic symptoms (rated at scale 6).

9. **Problems with emotional and related symptoms**

- Rates only the most severe clinical problems not considered previously.
- Includes depression, anxiety, worries, fears, phobias, obsessions or compulsions, arising from any clinical condition including eating disorders.
- Does not include aggressive, destructive or overactive behaviours attributed to fears and phobias (rated at scale 1).
- Does not include physical complications of psychological disorders, such as severe weight loss (rated at scale 6).

10. Problems with peer relationships

- Includes problems with school mates and social network. Problems associated with active to passive withdrawal from social relationships or problems with over-intrusiveness or problems with the ability to form satisfying peer relationships.

- Includes social rejection as a result of aggressive behaviour or bullying.

- Does not include aggressive behaviour, bullying (rated at scale 1), or problems with family or siblings (rated at scale 12).

11. Problems with self-care and independence

- Rates the overall level of functioning: e.g. problems with basic activities of self-care such as feeding, washing, dressing, toilet, also complex skills such as managing money, travelling independently, shopping etc., taking into account the norm for the child's chronological age.

- Includes poor levels of functioning arising from lack of motivation.

- Does not include lack of opportunities for exercising intact abilities and skills, as might occur in an over-restrictive family (rated at scale 12); somatic components of enuresis and encopresis (rated at scale 8). Only rates additional self-care problems associated with these disorders.

12. Problems with family life and relationships

- Includes parent-child and sibling relationship problems. Includes relationships with foster parents and with social workers/teachers in residential placements. Relationships in the home and with separated parents/siblings are both included.

- Includes problems with communication and emotional involvement. Includes problems associated with family reorganisation such as following bereavement, breakdown or relocation. Parental personality problems, mental illness, marital difficulties should be rated here only if they have an effect on the child.

- Includes problems of emotional abuse such as verbal hostility, criticism and denigration, parental neglect/rejection, over-restriction.

- Includes sexual and/or physical abuse. Includes sibling jealousy, physical or coercive sexual abuse by sibling.

- Does not include aggressive behaviour by child (rated at scale 1).

13. Poor school attendance

- Includes truancy, school refusal, school withdrawal or suspension for any cause.

References

1. NHS Health Advisory Service, *Together We Stand: The commissioning, role and management of child and adolescent mental health services*, HMSO, 1995.

2. M Target, P Fonagy, 'The psychological treatment of child and adolescent psychiatric disorder', pp. 263-320, in A Roth, P Fonagy (eds), *What Works for Whom? A Critical Review of Psychotherapy Research*, The Guilford Press, New York, 1996.

3. M Rutter, D J Smith (eds), *Psychosocial Disorders in Young People: Time Trends and their Causes*, John Wiley & Sons on behalf of Academia Europaea, 1995.

4. M Rutter, E Taylor, L Hersov (eds), Preface, *Child and Adolescent Psychiatry: Modern Approaches* (3rd edition), Blackwell Scientific Publications, 1994.

5. M Rutter et al., 'Attainment and adjustment in two geographical areas – 1: The prevalence of psychiatric disorder', *British Journal of Psychiatry*, Vol. 126, 1975, pp493-509.

6. S Wallace et al., 'Child and adolescent mental health', pp55-128, in A Stevens, J Raftery (eds), *Health Care Needs Assessment: the epidemiologically based needs assessment reviews*, Radcliffe Medical Press, Oxford and New York, 1997.

7. I Kolvin et al., 'Risk/Protective factors for offending with particular reference to deprivation', pp77-95 in M Rutter (ed.) *Studies of Psychosocial Risk: The Power of Longitudinal Data*. Cambridge University Press, 1988.

8. J McCann et al., 'Prevalence of psychiatric disorders in young people in the care system', *British Medical Journal*, Vol. 313, 1996, pp1529-30.

9. M Rutter, D Quinton, 'Parental psychiatric disorder: Effects on children', *Psychological Medicine*, Vol. 14, 1984, pp853-80.

10. M Rutter, H Giller, A Hagell, *Antisocial Behaviour by Young People*, Cambridge University Press, 1998.

11. J Gunn, A Maden, M Swinton, 'Treatment needs of prisoners with psychiatric disorders', *British Medical Journal*, Vol. 303, 1991.

12. I Holloway et al., *Health Status of Juvenile Offenders – a survey of young offenders appearing before the juvenile courts*, Paper presented to International Congress of Law and Psychology, Siena, Italy, 1996.

13. P Graham, 'Behavioural and intellectual development in childhood epidemiology', *British Medical Bulletin*, Vol. 42, 1986, pp155-62.

14. J Barnes, 'Mental health promotion: a developmental perspective', *Psychology, Health & Medicine*, Vol. 3(1), 1998, pp55-69.

15. M Bone, H Meltzer, The Prevalence of Disability among Children, *OPCS Surveys of Disability in Great Britain*. Report 3, HMSO, 1989.

16. D Farrington, R Loeber, w B van Kammen, 'Long-term criminal outcomes of hyperactivity-impulsivity-attention deficit and conduct disorder in childhood', pp62-81, in L Robins, M Rutter (eds), *Straight and Devious Pathways from Childhood to Adulthood*, Cambridge University Press, 1990.

17. Department of Health and Department for Education, *A Handbook on Child and Adolescent Mental Health*, HMSO, 1995.

18. R Williams, Personal Communication, 1999.

19. D Offord et al., 'Ontario Child Health Study-II. Six-month prevalence of disorder and rates of service utilization'. *Archives of General Psychiatry*, Vol. 44, 1987, pp832-6.

20. P Leaf et al., 'Mental health service use in the community and schools: results from the four-community MECA study', *Journal of the American Academy of Child and Adolescent Psychiatry*, Vol. 35, 1996, pp889-97.

21. Z Kurtz, R Thornes, S Wolkind, *Services for the mental health of children and young people in England: A national review*, Department of Health, 1994.

22. Department for Education, *Pupils with Problems*, Circulars 8-13, 1994.

23. Department of Health, *Child Protection: Messages from Research*, HMSO, 1995.

24. *Children's Services Planning Guidance*, EL(96)28 and LAC(96)10.

25. NHS Executive, *Priorities and Planning Guidance for the NHS*, 1996/97

26. House of Commons Select Committee on Health, Fourth Report *Child and Adolescent Mental Health Services*, 1997.

27. Welsh Office, *The Health of Children in Wales*, 1997.

28. Welsh Office, *Child & Adolescent Mental Health Resources Assessment – Wales*, Value For Money Unit, 1998.

29. Department for Education and Employment, *Meeting Special Educational Needs: a programme for action*, 1998.

30. House of Commons Select Committee on Health, *Children Looked After by Local Authorities*, 1998.

31. The Quality Protects Programme: *Transforming Children's Services*, LAC(98)28.

32. *Supporting Families*, The Government's Green Paper on Family Policy, The Stationery Office, 1998.

33. Department of Health, *Our Healthier Nation*, The Stationery Office, 1998.

34. *Inequalities in Health*, Report of an Independent Inquiry (Chairman: Sir Donald Acheson), The Stationery Office, 1998.

35. Department of Health, Health Service Circular and Local Authority Circular, *NHS Modernisation Fund and Mental Health Grant for Child and Adolescent Mental Health Services 1999/2002*, HSC 1999/126: LAC (99)22, 21 May 1999.

36. Department of Health, *Modernising Health and Social Service: National Priorities Guidance 1999/00 to 2001/02*, 1998.

37. P Fonagy et al., *The Effectiveness of Interventions for Child and Adolescent Mental Health: a systematic review of the literature*, Wiley (in preparation) 2000.

38. Z Kurtz (ed.), 'With Health in Mind', Action for Sick Children, 1992.

39. V Soni Raleigh, R Balaraja, 'The health of infants and children among ethnic minorities', pp.82-94, in B Botting (ed.), *The Health of Our Children,* OPCS Decennial Supplement, series DS no. 11, HMSO, 1995.

40. S Gowers et al., 'A brief scale for measuring the outcomes of emotional and behavioural disorders in children: the Health of the Nation Outcome Scales for Children and Adolescents (HoNOSCA)', *British Journal of Psychiatry*, Vol. 174, 1999, pp413-16.

41. P Yates, M Garralda, I Higginson, 'Paddington Complexity Scale and Health of the Nation Outcome Scales for Children and Adolescents', *British Journal of Psychiatry*, Vol. 174, 1999, pp417-23.

42. Office for National Statistics, *Social Trends Volume 28*, The Stationery Office, 1998.

43. D Goldberg, P Huxley, *Mental Illness in the Community: The Pathway to Psychiatric Care*, Tavistock, 1980.

44. Department of Health, *Children looked after by Local Authorities*, July 1998.

45. A Whitaker, J Johnson, D Shaffer, 'Uncommon troubles in young people: prevalence estimates of selected psychiatric disorders in a non-referred adolescent population', *Archives of General Psychiatry*, Vol. 47, 1990, pp487-96.

46. C Caron, M Rutter, 'Comorbidity in child psychopathology: Concepts, issues and research strategies', *Journal of Child Psychology and Psychiatry*, Vol. 32, 1990, pp1063-80.

47. B Jarman, 'Identification of underprivileged areas', *British Medical Journal*, Vol. 286, 1983, pp1705-9.

48.   Audit Commission, *Higher Purchase: Commissioning Specialised Services in the NHS*, Audit Commission, 1998.

49.   Department of Health, *Commissioning in the new NHS*, Health Service Circular 198, 1998.

50.   Child Psychotherapy Trust, *Is Child Psychotherapy Effective for Children and Young People?*, 1998.

51.   Child Psychotherapy Trust, *With Children in Mind*, 1998.

52.   Child Psychotherapy Trust, *Promoting Infant Mental Health*, July 1999.

53.   Audit Commission, *Misspent Youth '99: The Challenge for Youth Justice*, Audit Commission, 1999.

54.   D Cottrell et al., 'Factors influencing non-attendance at child psychiatry out-patient appointments', *British Journal of Psychiatry*, Vol. 152, 1988, pp201-4.

55.   M Knapp, S Scott, J Davies, 'The cost of anti-social behaviour in younger children: A pilot study of economic and family impact', *Clinical Child Psychology and Psychiatry*, forthcoming 1999.

56.   R Goodman, 'Child and Adolescent Mental Health Services: Reasoned Advice to Commissioners and Providers', *Maudsley Discussion Paper No. 4*. Institute of Psychiatry.

57.   C Armstrong, M Hill, J Secker, *Listening to Children*, Mental Health Foundation, 1998.

58.   M Fisher, 'Adolescent inpatient units', *Archives of Disease in Childhood*, Vol. 70, 1994, pp461-3.

59.   S Law, *Hear Me*, Mental Health Foundation, 1998.

60.   A Hopkins, *Measuring the Quality of Medical Care*, Royal College of Physicians, 1990.

61.   Z Kurtz, *Treating Children Well*, Mental Health Foundation, 1996.

62.   J Weisz et al., 'Child and adolescent psychotherapy outcomes in experiments versus clinics: Why the disparity?', *Journal of Abnormal Child Psychology*, Vol. 23, 1995, pp83-106.

63.   K Hoagwood et al., 'Outcomes of mental health care for children and adolescents: A comprehensive conceptual model', *Journal of the American Academy of Child and Adolescent Psychiatry*, Vol. 35, 1996, pp1055-63.

64.   L Bickman et al., 'A continuum of care: More is not always better', *American Psychologist*, Vol. 51, 1996, pp689-701.

65.   H Davis et al., 'Child and adolescent mental health needs in an inner city area', *Clinical Child Psychology and Psychiatry* (submitted for publication), 1999.

66.   M Berger et al., 'A proposed core data set for child and adolescent psychology and psychiatry services', *Association for Child Psychology and Psychiatry*, 1993.

67.   C Day, H Davis, R Hind, 'The development of a community child and family mental health service', *Child Care, Health and Development*, Vol. 24, 1998, pp 487-500.

68.   M Rutter, J Tizard, K Whitmore (eds), *Education, Health and Behaviour*, Longmans, 1970.

69.   M Rutter, P Graham, W Yule, *A Neuropsychiatric Study in Childhood*, Heinemann, 1970.

70.   M Rutter, 'Isle of Wight revisited: Twenty-five years of child psychiatric epidemiology', *Journal of the American Academy of Child and Adolescent Psychiatry*, Vol. 28, 1989, pp633-53.

71.   J Pearce, S Holmes, 'Health Gain Investment Programme', Technical Review Document. *People with Mental Health Problems (part four) – Child and Adolescent Mental Health*, NHS Executive Trent and Centre for Mental Health Services Development, 1994.

Index References are to paragraph numbers, Boxes, Case Studies and Appendices